THE VISITORS

Arr

GW01045604

Lindsey Porter

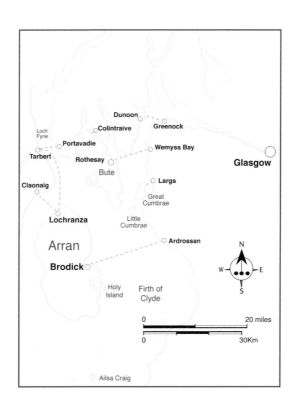

Published by
**Guidelines Books & Sales**
11 Belmont Road, Ipstones, Stoke on Trent ST10 2JN
☎ 07971 990649 email: author.porter@gmail.com

ISBN 978-1-84306-551-7

Printed by Berforts Information Press Ltd, Eynsham, Oxford

**Disclaimer**
While every care has been taken to ensure that the information in this book is as accurate as possible at the time of publication, the publisher accepts no responsibility for any loss, injury or inconvenience etc sustained by anyone using this book.

**Cover captions: Front:** Machrie Bay; **Back: left:** Brodick Beach; **right:** Blackwaterfoot

Goatfell looking north. In the middle of the ridge in shadow is the Witches Step with the Castles to the left of it (photo: Chris Mills)

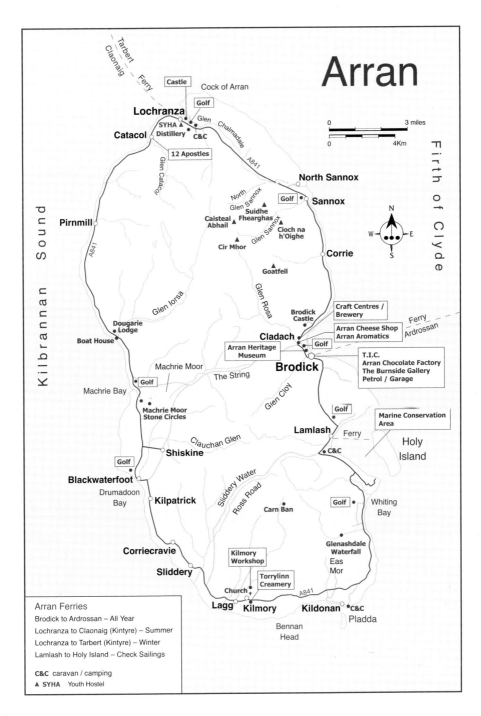

# Arran

**Castle**
Cock of Arran

**Golf**

**Lochranza**
Glen
Chalmadale

SYHA ▲
Glen
**Catacol** ○ Distillery **C&C**

**12 Apostles**

A841

**North Sannox**

North
Glen Sannox **Golf** ● **Sannox**

Caisteal ▲ **Suidhe**
Abhail **Fhearghas** ▲

Cioch na
h'Oighe

Glen Sannox

Cir Mhor ▲

**Corrie** ▲

Goatfell ▲

Glen Iorsa

Dougarie
● Lodge

Boat House

Glen Rosa

Brodick
Castle

**Craft Centres /
Brewery**

**Cladach** ○

**Arran Cheese Shop
Arran Aromatics**

**Golf**

Ferry
Ardrossan

**Arran Heritage
Museum**

**Brodick**

**T.I.C.
Arran Chocolate Factory
The Burnside Gallery
Petrol / Garage**

Machrie Moor
The String

Glen Cloy

**Golf** ●
Machrie Bay

**Golf** ●

**Lamlash**
Ferry

**Marine Conservation
Area**

Machrie Moor
Stone Circles

● **C&C**

Holy
Island

Clauchan Glen
**Shiskine**

**Golf** ●

**Blackwaterfoot** ○

Drumadoon
Bay **Kilpatrick**

Sliddery Water
Ross Road

Carn Ban ●

**Golf** ●
Whiting
Bay

**Corriecravie**

Kilmory
Workshop

Glenashdale
Waterfall

**Sliddery** ○

Torrylinn
Creamery

Eas
Mor

Church
**Lagg** **Kilmory**

A841

**Kildonan** ○ **C&C**
Pladda

Bennan
Head

Kilbrannan Sound

**Pirnmill** ○

A841

0            3 miles
0            4Km

N
W ● ● ● E
S

Firth of Clyde

## Arran Ferries

Brodick to Ardrossan – All Year

Lochranza to Claonaig (Kintyre) – Summer

Lochranza to Tarbert (Kintyre) – Winter

Lamlash to Holy Island – Check Sailings

**C&C**  caravan / camping
▲ **SYHA**  Youth Hostel

Tarbert
Claonaig
Ferry

# Arran

Arran is situated south west of Glasgow, Scotland, in the Firth of Clyde. It is the largest of a small group of islands, sheltering Bute and Great & Little Cumbrae to the north east. Off its southern shore is the dramatic form of Ailsa Craig, an island looking like an upturned cone, halfway between Glasgow and Belfast.

Arran had a population of 5,058 in 2001 (in 1901 it was 4,819). It is 20 miles/32 km long and 8.5-10 miles/13.6-16 km in width. Much of the development is on or close to the coast, leaving the rugged and mountainous interior largely untouched except for areas of forest. Although there are no Munros here, Goatfell rises to 2,865 ft/874m and is clearly visible (allowing for low cloud) from Brodick, creating a memorable vista with Brodick Castle in the mid-distance across the bay.

Arran has several large bays around its coast and Lamlash Bay is one of the finest natural harbours in Britain, being sheltered by Holy Island. The latter rises to just over 1,030ft/314 m, the island appearing quite dramatically a little way off shore, especially if you are driving from Whiting Bay. It is 2miles/3.2kmin length and up to ⅔rds mile /1km in breadth.

Approaching Brodick at the end of the day, with Beinn Nuis in the distance

Brodick Castle from the Shore Road, Brodick

## Getting There

The rugged interior landscape, mountains and scenic coastline makes Arran a popular destination. By Cal Mac ferry it is only 55 minutes from Ardrossan on the Ayrshire coast across to Brodick or 30 minutes to Lochranza from Claonaig on the Kintyre coast. Note that there is a reduced winter service and the Claonaig ferry is replaced by one crossing each day between Tarbert and Lochranza (no service 25th-26th December and 1st-2nd January. Reservations are essential for this winter service. Book on 0800 066 5000 or online at www.calmac.co.uk). There are no trains or airport on Arran but there is a heliport east of the Cal Mac jetty at Brodick. Ardrossan is served by trains from Glasgow Central. Arran has a good bus network, check with Tourist Information for the timetable (☎ 01770 303774).

## Ten good reasons to go to Arran

Only 55 minutes away by efficient Cal Mac ferry.

Enjoy the experience of Scottish West Coast island heritage: castles, cairns and standing stones give a sense of the depth of history on the island.

Lots to do for families: sandy bays and exciting rock pools for children; many traffic free areas; activities for the young at heart; pony trekking; upland, lowland and mountain walking.

Shopping for local produce.

Sport; a different golf course each day of the week; mountaineering; water sports; fishing; cycling around the island etc to name but a few.

Wildlife: red squirrels everywhere; look out for the deer and eagles, especially in the north; seals – especially around Kildonan in the south. There is a marine conservation area at Lamlash Bay.

Fine dining on locally caught fish and seafood, some smoked on the island; local venison etc.

Accommodation: plenty to suit your taste and pocket.

Friendly, helpful residents

Photographic opportunities galore.

# Brodick

There is no central market place here. Everything is on the seafront so far as the commercial heart of the town is concerned. The ferry terminal is at the eastern end of Shore Road, almost opposite the **Tourist Information Centre**. The retail outlets are mainly on Shore Road, enjoying the view out into **Brodick Bay**. Amongst the largest buildings is the upmarket and recently refurbished Douglas Hotel, built of local red sandstone, which is separated from another large building, the Co-op, by the Douglas Centre Shopping mall. This parade of commercial, chiefly retail, buildings includes the Royal Bank of Scotland and the Bank of Scotland (both with an ATM, as is the Co-op). Car parking is free,

Next to the Tourist Information Centre is the Petrol Station. Continue along the street heading east if you want Angus Lambie's local garage/recovery

The Information Centre, opposite the Cal Mac jetty, Brodick

Arran Heritage Centre is definitely worth visiting

service. The **Health Centre** is in Shore Road and the **Post Office** in Alma Road, virtually opposite the car park and chemist at the western end of Shore Road.

There is a narrow but convenient promenade along the shoreline, with free car parking between that and the road. With the commercial properties set well back, the frontage has a pleasing air about it, even when the distant view is restricted by low cloud and rain. Given sunshine and blue sky, Brodick Bay takes some beating for its vista.

# To Lochranza

Taking Shore Road, you pass a car park on your right (near the Co-op shop at the western end of the road (not the supermarket). Here you can gain access to the sandy **Brodick beach**, just prior to reaching the **Golf Club House**. Here too is the start of **Fisherman's Walk**, a two mile long combined path for walkers and cyclists, which leads to Brodick Castle, taking in the beach, the shops and restaurant at Home Farm (including Duchess Court). Beyond here is a further group of shops at Cladach, including a Visitor Centre. Behind this are various outlets, including the brewery (see below) and the pedestrian entrance to the Castle. The whole distance, on the flat, is about 2miles/ 3.2 km.

A little further along Shore Road (A 841) and on the right is the **Arran Heritage Museum**, giving an insight into the island's history. It has a riverside garden and café. [Contact: Roseburn, Brodick, KA278DP, ☎ 01770 302636, www. arranmuseum.co.uk] There is a large car park at the road side. Beyond here, the A 880 goes ahead (strictly a left turn) to the west coast and the A 841 takes a sharp right. Just beyond, look out for the **Duchess Court** and **Home Farm shops** on the right.

This complex includes the **Arran Aromatic's factory shop**, selling fragrances, soaps, and other toiletries, candles etc. There are factory tours (Thursdays, 6-8pm), candle making for children and the opportunity to pamper yourself a little. [Contact: Home Farm, Brodick, KA27 8DD, ☎ 01770 303003, www. arranaromatics.com] Don't overlook the Duchess Court shops and coffee shop, Arran Cheese, Creelers Seafood Restaurant plus their shop selling smoked seafood. The **Island Cheese Company** produces eight wax-sealed

Arran Aromatics and the Duchess Court plus the Home Farm Shops adjacent are well worth including on your itinerary

The Arran Aromatics shop, where you can indulge yourself for a while
(photo: Arran Aromatics)

flavoured Cheddar Cheeses [Contact: 01770 302788, www.arrancheeseshop.co.uk Look out for these on mainland Scottish Farmers' markets too; **Creelers Smokehouse and shop**, Home Farm, Brodick, KA27 8DD, ☎ 01770 302797, www.creelers.co.uk]

Some 350 yards further on is the Cladach car park and the start of one of the **Goatfell** paths, opposite the **Wineport bar** and restaurant. Adjacent to it is the brewery, together with shops selling leather goods, outdoor clothing and equipment, wood carvings, architectural glass and the **Cladach Pottery**.

**Arran Brewery** has a visitor centre with guided or self guided tours. You can sample different brews and the shop gives you the chance to purchase more. Most of the brewing is done between 10.30am –1.30pm, Monday-Friday, but the visitor centre is open until 5pm. It is not open on Sundays and Tuesdays in the winter and then with restricted opening times. [Contact: Arran Brewery, Cladach, Brodick, ☎ 01770 302353, www.arranbrewery.com]

# Brodick Castle

By the Wineport is the pedestrian entrance to the Castle. Steeped in history, it is associated with Robert the Bruce. Kings Cave on the West Coast was where he saw, while in hiding, the spider repeatedly trying to make its web, overcoming its difficulties and giving him the incentive to do the same. Occupied by the Dukes of Hamilton for over 500 years, it passed to the Duke of Montrose on the marriage of Lady Mary Douglas-Hamilton in 1906. At that time she owned the whole island with the exception of the 3,632 acre Kirkmichael Estate.

The castle passed to the National Trust for Scotland in 1958 and is the principal man made attraction on the island. Much of the current structure dates from a large extension of the building in 1844. The National Trust Estate also includes Goatfell, which is open daily, subject to weather conditions. The latter can make an attempt on the summit life threatening and in any event, the path should not be taken without the appropriate clothing, footwear and adequate provisions. The house is well known for its collection of furniture and fine art and the extensive gardens are equally worth a visit.

Arran Brewery (left) is one of several outlets at Cladach, just beyond Duchess Court. The Wineport and Bistro is also located here along with several other shops and the pedestrian entrance to Brodick Castle

Brodick Castle (photo: Chris Mills)

[☎ 0844 493 2152, www.nts.org.uk/property/brodick-castle The Castle is not open Nov-March and the walled garden is open daily April-Oct and Nov-20th Dec Sat-Sun only]

# North of the Castle

Beyond the Castle, the road hugs the coast as it runs north passed the fringe of the Forestry Commission's **Merkland Forest**. There are places to park and forest trails to explore here. Just before you reach the little settlement of **Corrie**, there is a pull-in by the sea with picnic tables: a great place to stop for a few minutes before reaching Corrie itself with its little harbour.

Just 1 ½ miles/2.4 km north of Corrie is **Sannox**, situated at **Sannox Bay**. Here is the **Corrie Golf Club**, with its tearoom (eat in or take away). All the island golf courses welcome tearoom visitors and some have a restaurant. The Sannox Bay Hotel looks out to sea and is useful if you want somewhere half way between Brodick and Lochranza or convenient for exploring the magnificent **Glen Sannox** behind Sannox village.

If you are seriously into mountain walks or believe you are fit enough and with a head for heights, you might like to consider the Isle of Arran Mountain Festival's Glen Sannox Horseshoe Epic. It incorporates six peaks, covering 10 miles/16 km with rock scrambles and steep slopes along the way. [☎ 01770 302244, www.arranmountainfestival.co.uk] Alternatively, if you are content with a stroll in stunning scenery, a walk from Sannox up the glen is a gentle climb, avoiding the serious part and a return back down to the village.

Yet another alternative is the pony trekking centre at **North Sannox** [☎ 01770 810222]. It is open daily except for Sundays. Turning off the Lochranza road for North Sannox takes you down to a car park (with toilets) and a large area of cut grass with seats (no tables). It passes the drive to the pony trekking centre on your left.

From Sannox, the road (A841) cuts north west for the 5½miles/8.8km to Lochranza. It climbs up the wide expanse of North Glen Sannox past the tree clothed An Tunna to the left before starting the descent down **Glen Chalmadale** to the coast. It is a drop of over 600ft/199m covering all of 2 miles/3.2 km. If you are cycling around the island, it is this section which may

**Above:** Corrie Village

**Above right:** Corrie from the harbour

**Right:** The tiny harbour at Corrie

**Below:** Suidhe Fhearghas towering above the entrance to Glen Sannox from the picnic area at North Sannox

influence your choice to do it anti-clockwise. You also get the benefit of the view down the glen and out to sea towards **Kintyre**.

At the foot of the glen is picturesque **Lochranza**, with one of the first principal buildings being the **distillery** on your left. It has made whisky since 1995, was opened by HM The Queen and is one of the few independent malt whisky makers in Scotland. Although a subjective matter, some say it makes some of the finest malts there are. Try a dram at the distillery and judge for yourself. It really is special. There are distillery tours, a café and shop (selling a range of local products in addition to whisky). [☎ 01770 830264. Open daily March–Oct and reduced hours in winter].

Before you reach the castle, you pass the **Lochranza Youth Hostel**, recently refurbished and the only one on the island. The most dominant feature of the village is the loch with its ruined castle. It is L-shaped and dates from the 16th century. Although a ruin, much of it does in fact survive. It is now cared for by Historic Scotland and is only open in the summer. The views from the castle down Loch Ranza or back up to the mountains are memorable. The island's most northerly golf course is at Lochranza.

The distillery sells a postcard showing male deer in the water by the castle at sunset. It is called Stag Night! Look therefore for red deer coming down to the loch shore and for the grey seals. If you are luckier still, you may see otters on the shoreline and also a couple of golden eagles high above the area of the distillery or closer to the mountains.

From the 2003-built pier, the car ferry to Claonaig on Kintyre gives an alternative way on and off the island in summer to the Brodick ferry. It still runs with a reduced service in winter, but to Tarbert.

At the east side of the sea-end of Loch Ranza is **Newton Point**. Here, a very early geologist, James Hutton, found rocks lying across older rocks and clearly not a continuation of deposits. It was one of the most important discoveries in the study of geology. Another interesting geological feature visible on the west coast is the raised beaches and cliffs of the former coastline before the land surface rose after the Ice Age. This happened because of the removal of the massive weight of the ice which had depressed the surface of the land. This is why The King's Cave, where Robert the Bruce observed the spider, is so much above sea level.

The Arran Distillery at Lochranza, opened in 1995

Loch Ranza with the castle in the middle to the left of the telegraph post (photo: Chris Mills)

# Lochranza to Blackwaterfoot

To the west of Lochranza, the coast road heads to the south west before turning south and running down to **Machrie**. The whole of the west side of the island faces Kintyre across **Kilbrannan Sound**. At the narrowest point, it is 3 miles/5 km across (Imachar to Carradale). The road is narrower and the surface (in places) not quite as good as that traversed so far.

Slightly over a mile out of Lochranza is **Catacol**, one of several very small communities on this coast. Its principle feature is a group of twelve terraced cottages, unusually known as **The Twelve Apostles**. Note that the gable windows are (or were) all different. A local fisherman would apparently know if he was wanted by a light shining from his window, recognising its unique shape! The terrace is at the side of the road just prior to reaching **Glen Catacol**. The latter runs in the south west direction, where its path rounds **Beinn Bheac**, gradually climbing in height to meet another path, which then runs north to Lochranza down **Gleann Easan Biorach**. The distance is 7 miles/ 12 km in all.

Lochranza Castle

Left: The Twelve Apostles, Catacol.  Right: Catacol Bay

Left: The raised beach and former sea-cliffs are a feature of the west coast. These are at Machrie,  Right: The north side of Lochranza castle (photo: H Maurice Jones)

Just beyond the mouth of the glen, the raised beach and cliffs may be seen, running intermittently for several miles above the road, although they are hidden in places by trees and shrubs. A little over 3 miles/5 km further on is **Pirnmill**, where waters draining from **Mullach Buidhe** and **Beinn Bharrain** (to its right) reach the sea. Both these peaks are of respectable height, being 2,365 ft/721m and 2,352 ft/717 m respectively. There is a village store, Post Office and restaurant at Pirnmill.

It is a similar distance from Pirnmill to **Dougarie Lodge**, the former summer house of the Dukes of Hamilton, set just back from the road and above the Iorsa Water, the river draining the 27,000 acre/10,927 ha estate. The Lodge was built in 1865. Note its substantial Boathouse by the slipway, between the road and the sea. Both the Lodge and the Boathouse are private. The Estate offers good quality holiday accommodation (including a luxurious country house) as well as providing a choice of activities from golf and fishing to field sports. [☎ 01770 840259, www.dougarie.com]

Ahead is **Machrie Bay**, with its golf course by the coast, the latter fringed by a largely stoney strip of shore. Just before the golf course is a sign to the left to the **Old Byre Showroom**. Here you can buy local hand knitted Aran (sic) Sweaters, quality knitwear, bags etc., outdoor wear as well as a snack or meal in the Café Thyme. It is open daily, 10-5pm.

Just beyond the golf course is an area described by Historic Scotland as one of the most important of its kind in Britain. Over a layer of Neolithic wooden hut circles are chambered tombs, a concentration of six **stone circles** and more hut circles all dating from the Bronze Age. The OS map shows a lot of these hut circles and that isn't the half of it. Moreover, there is very little to see on the ground of them. Nonetheless they point to a concentration of population in those far off times. There are also two prehistoric forts, one just north of **Drumadoon Point**, which is adjacent to **Shiskine Golf Course**. The other may be seen due east of this one, on the top of **Cnoc Ballygown**, some 2 miles/3.2 km away. Cnoc is Celtic for small hill.

Looking north to Dougarie

Sunset at Machrie Bay, looking towards Kintyre with Carradale on the far left

The Moss Farm Road stone circle, on the track to the other Machrie Moor stone circles

Left: Dougarie Point with raised seacliffs in the mid-distance. Taken from the north end of Machrie Bay  Right: Blackwaterfoot, with its tiny harbour

If there is little to see of the hut circles, that is not the case with the stone circles as some include tall standing stones, one of which is 18 ft/5.5 m in height. Just south of the golf course there is a double bend in the road, incorporating a small bridge over the Machrie Water, a small stream. Just beyond this and with little warning, there is a small car park on the right opposite a farm tack to the now ruined Moss Farm, which is adjacent to the stone circles.

Allowing for field access by the farmer, there is not much room here and you may find it full. It is a pity it is not larger for the 1½ mile walk is worth the effort if only for the view on the way back! Take the Moss Farm track. After about 10 minutes, you pass the Moss Farm Road stone circle on the right with the rest further up the track. Don't forget your camera, the circles can be quite evocative, especially if the light is right.

From the golf course, a road goes inland to join the road across the island to Brodick (B 880). The coast road meanwhile continues south for another 3 miles/ 5km to **Blackwaterfoot**, a small, chiefly modern–built, community with the Kinloch Hotel, a gallery, grocer, post office and repair garage. It also has the Siskine golf course. It is unusual in two respects: it has 12 holes and the course borders the sand dunes at the edge of the beach. A path goes passed the golf course and carries on up the coast to Tormore, passing **The King's Cave** and its association with Robert the Bruce.

Blackwaterfoot is the home of the Cairnhouse riding centre, for novices and experienced riders. [Contact: The Stables, Blackwaterfoot, KA27 8EU, ☎ 01770 860466]. From Blackwaterfoot, the B 880 runs back to Brodick through Siskine and Ballymichael.

Lagg Hotel with its ancient inn of 1791

# Blackwaterfoot to Lamlash & Brodick

The coastal road continues to **Sliddery** and the Sliddery Water river, dropping down to cross the mouth of the glen before reaching **Lagg**. The Ross Road, a minor, narrow road goes up the glen to Lamlash, a useful short cut. The southern half of Ross Road runs through open moorland whilst the northern half skirts or cuts through forest.

Lagg gives you the opportunity to stop for refreshments at its picturesque and charming Lagg inn/hotel. It is situated by a stream, the **Kilmory Water** which abuts the attractive garden to the rear. Immediately on crossing the bridge outside the inn a signpost to the right directs you to a chambered tomb above the coast. It is only a few minutes walk (parking is not easy). To either side of the tomb (or cairn) remains of the former cliffs can be seen, now raised above the beach. Just beyond Lagg is **Kilmory** and the **Torrylinn Creamery**. Here cheese is produced and you can buy it in the factory shop there. [☎ 01770 870240, www.highlandsandislandscheese.co.uk Open: Apl–Sept 9.30–4.30, Mon–Fri (and Sat in July–Aug), reduced winter times]

At the crossroads near to the Creamery, a left turn brings you to the parish church. There are many ancient gravestones here together with a copy of the figurehead of the *Bessie Arnold*, which foundered near here with the loss of her crew of five. The churchyard copy is made of marble and the original is in the church, which is usually kept locked.

Signposted along the road to the church and a little further on is the **Kilmory Workshop**, producing and selling handmade woodwork and pottery, including furniture and toys plus stoneware pottery. [☎ 01770 870310, www. kilmoryworkshop.co.uk Open: Tues–Fri, 10.00–5.30pm]

Beyond Kilmory, when views of the sea permit, start looking for the dramatic island of **Ailsa Craig** rising unexpectedly out of the sea. If you are after a photograph – it can be quite a dramatic view on a clear day – continue to Kildonan where you can take the island of Pladda in the foreground with its lighthouse.

**Kildonan** is situated off the island ring road and on the west side, a loop road drops down hill to the coastal community, rising back again on the east side. There are hotels, a couple of car parks and a castle ruin plus the **Seal Shore**

Left: Kilmory Church  Right: The replica figurehead of the *Bessie Arnold* at Kilmory Churchyard

**Camping and Caravan site** with 10 electric hook-ups and shop [☎ 01770 820320, www.campingarran.com]. The south end bus (No. 323) stops at the site entrance on request.

The name of the site, Seal Shore, is not some marketing feature. Kildonan is the best place to see seals on Arran. Take the coastal path in the village, you may be well rewarded, but do leave them alone and don't try to get too close.

Upon reaching the T-junction where the road is signposted to the right for Kildonan as mentioned above, there is a small car park and a footpath to the small gorge called **Eas Mor**. It is less than a mile to it (on foot) and it is quite dramatic with its vertical walls crowned by trees and with a view back to the sea and the island of **Pladda**. The car park is 4 miles/6.5 km from the Creamery.

# Ailsa Craig

Rising out of the entrance to the Firth of Clyde is the small but very dramatic island of Ailsa Craig to a height of 1,114ft/338 m in height. Known as Paddy's Milestone, it is halfway between Glasgow and Belfast and just south of Arran. It rises shear sided initially and then slopes up to the central point, like an inverted cone. The island is all that remains of the core of an ancient volcano.

It was once the home to the lighthouse keeper and the former granite quarry swelled the population to 29 people by the end of the Victorian era. However by 1904, the population was down to just four. The quarry worked riebeckite, a black stone used for ornate building work. You can see it in the floor of the Chapel of the Thistle in St Giles' Cathedral in Edinburgh. Another more unusual use was for curling stones, including those used by the Scottish Womens' team when they won the gold medal at the winter Olympics in 2002.

The lighthouse was built in 1886 by Thomas Stevenson and his nephew David. Thomas was the father of Robert Louis Stevenson, the writer. Now the lighthouse is automated and the island is uninhabited. Prior to the lighthouse having a wireless telegraph machine installed in 1935, pigeons and even fires were used to summon assistance from the mainland.

Today the island is a Site of Special Scientific Interest and is the home of over 70,000 breeding seabirds of which nearly half are gannets. The rest are chiefly guillemots and black guillemots, razor bills and puffins. Brown rats had wiped out the puffins by 1934, but an eradication programme removed them. Now the puffins are thriving again. The RSPB has managed a reserve here since 2004 and do not permit dogs to land (except guide dogs). There are no facilities (other than the jetty) and no formal arrangements about landing. To view the birds at their best, there is no need to land.

### Getting there from Arran

Contact Ocean Breeze Wildlife & Sightseeing Tours from Arran, ☎ 07771 463567/07837 338874, www.obrt.co.uk E: skipper@obt.co.uk Tours usually from the Old Pier, Lamlash, KA27 8JN

Ailsa Craig rising out of the sea on a stormy day

Whiting Bay

Holy Island from Whiting Bay

A few minutes beyond Kildonan, upon returning to the Lagg-**Whiting Bay** road is the latter village, on the west coast. Here there are stores, a garage serving petrol etc and an attractive, long and narrow sandy beach. Immediately before where the Glenashdale Burn reaches the sea, a left turn brings you to a car park. From here, there is a walk of a mile or so up the side of the river to **Glenashdale Falls**. You can either return the way you came or cross the glen and return down the other side. From Whiting Bay, the road improves in width and quality.

No sooner have you left Whiting Bay and **Holy Island** looms up dramatically just off shore. The island is now a Buddhist retreat and welcomes visitors but not dogs (except guide dogs). The ferry boat leaves the Old Pier at Lamlash but it is a summer only service. [Contact: Holy Island Ferry: ☎ 01770 600998/700463 or 07970 771960, E: tomin10@btinternet.com] If you are looking for fishing tackle, bait, nautical clothing and footwear, plus maritime/Arran books (including those out of print), try Johnson's Maritime Stores on the Old Pier.

Just prior to reaching Lamlash, there is a sharp bend in the road to the right and a T-junction on the left with the Ross Road. Here is **Arran Fine Foods**

Holy Island shrouded in mist
(left) and a few minutes later
(above). Lamlash Bay is a Marine
Conservation Area

**Below:** The dramatic outline of
Holy Island from south of Lamlash

with its gift shop and factory outlet. [☎ 01770 600606, Open: daily, 9.30-5pm, Mon-Fri and 10-4pm weekends]

The area between Arran and Holy Island is a **Marine Conservation Area.** Much of it is a No Take Zone with marine life protected in one of the country's main natural harbours south of Scapa Flow. This means all fishing, personal and commercial. Naval ships used this harbour during the World Wars and it is still worth looking out for naval activity around the shores of Arran. It is common to see submarines on the surface, either on exercises or on the approach/departure from Holy Loch.

Just past the Ross Road junction there is a turning to the right for the **Corden Caravan and Camping site**. Just beyond here you reach **Lamlash**. This is undoubtedly the most attractive village on the island. It has managed to retain its Victorian charm and character and is a delight to explore. Like Whiting Bay, it has a variety of shops and several restaurants to suit your preference.

Lamlash

If you are playing the round of seven golf courses, your last one is just at the north end of the village. The site climbs the hill north of Lamlash, affording magnificent view of Lamlash Bay and Holy Island. The coast road continues along the shore past the turn for Brodick, but ends at **Claughland's Point**. It's worth taking if you are looking for seals and birdlife. The A 841 climbs up the side of the golf course into the forested **Claughland Hills** (there is a car park and scenic view, towards Goatfell, on the left at the top) before descending to Brodick.

# Additional Information

## Accommodation

If you are looking for accommodation, try the Tourist Information Centre first: ☎ 01770 303774. It is situated across the road from the ferry terminal at Brodick.

## Eating Out

(phone code in all cases is 01770)

Perhaps the three main restaurants in the Brodick are the centrally situated Douglas Hotel (302968); Creelers (302810) at Home Farm (close to Arran Aromatics); and Auchrannie Hotel and Country Club. There are also others at various hotels as well as Chinese and Indian restaurants.

Out of Brodick, it is worth remembering to check availability at the golf courses and there are hotels strategically placed on the A 841: eg Corrie Hotel [and the Sannox Bay Restaurant] in the north east; the café at the Distillery (830264) at Lochranza plus the Lochranza Hotel (830223) and Catacol Hotel in the north; the Lighthouse Restaurant at Pirnmill in the north west; the Thyme café (840227) at the Old Byre, mid-way down the west coast; the Kinloch Hotel (860444) Blackwaterfoot; the Lagg Hotel (870255) in the south; Kildonan Hotel (820207) in the south east and several places to eat in Whiting Bay and Lamlash.

One of the advantages of Arran is the number of restaurants offering local fish and other seafood. Creelers has its own smoke house.

## Golf Courses

Brodick ☎ 01770 302349
Corrie ☎ 01770 810223
Lochranza ☎ 01770 830273
Machrie ☎ 01770 840329
Shiskine ☎ 01770 860226; Felicitys
    Restaurant ☎ 860777
Whiting Bay ☎ 01770 700487;
Lamlash ☎ 01770 600196;
    Gorsebush Restaurant ☎ 600296

Machrie Golf Course, one of seven, giving the challenge of one course a day for a week

## Medical

Health Centre, Brodick ☎ 01770 600777
Hospital, Lamlash ☎ 01770 302175

## Petrol/Diesel

It is suggested that you keep plenty of fuel in your tank to avoid potential problems. There are not many petrol stations and none operate a 24 hour service.

## Shopping

There are no large shopping malls on Arran and only one large supermarket (the Co-op). There are plenty of opportunities to buy local products. Perhaps the most obvious are the malt whisky and beer, but look out for the local cheese, chocolates plus smoked seafood at the smokery adjacent to Creeler's restaurant at Duchess Court. In the same shopping complex you can by varied products from lovely scented soaps to sprays at Arran Aromatics. Just a little further up the road is another shopping complex with a pottery, leather goods outlet and an outdoor clothing specialist at Cladach. There are also a whole range of outlets in Shore Road, Brodick, plus banks (with ATMs) and the health centre.

The skyline shows the Witches Step (the pronounced dip), with the Castles to the right. The road is descending to Lochranza. Glen Sannox is beyond the far ridge (photo: Chris Mills)

The Cal Mac ferry *Caledonian Isles* approaching Brodick jetty from Ardrossan

# INDEX

# *The G*

## MARIO PUZO

Level 4

Retold by Chris Rice
Series Editors: Andy Hopkins and Jocelyn Potter

04428173

**Pearson Education Limited**
Edinburgh Gate, Harlow,
Essex CM20 2JE, England
and Associated Companies throughout the world.

ISBN: 978-1-4058-8219-4

First published in Great Britain by Random House UK Ltd 1969
This adaptation published by Penguin Books 1998
Published by Addison Wesley Longman Ltd and Penguin Books Ltd 1998
New edition first published 1999
This edition first published 2008

9  10

Typeset by Graphicraft Ltd, Hong Kong
Set in 11/14pt Bembo
Printed in China
SWTC/09

**Acknowledgements**
The publisher would like to thank the following
for their kind permission to reproduce their photographs:
**Rex Shutterstock:** Paramount / Kobal 19, 33, 43;
**The Kobal Collection:** Paramount Pictures 5, 13, 16, 30, 41, 53
**Cover images:** *Front and back:* **Shutterstock.com:** Marcin Roszkowski; **CD Cover:** *Onbody:*
**Shutterstock.com:** Marcin Roszkowski

Published by Pearson Education Ltd

*Every effort has been made to trace the copyright holders and we apologise in advance for any unintentional omissions.
We would be pleased to insert the appropriate acknowledgement in any subsequent edition of this publication.*

For a complete list of the titles available in the Pearson English Readers series, visit
www.pearsonenglishreaders.com.
Alternatively, write to your local Pearson Education office or to Pearson English Readers
Marketing Department, Pearson Education, Edinburgh Gate, Harlow, Essex CM20 2JE, England.

# *Contents*

# Introduction

*'My father made him an offer he couldn't refuse. Luca held a gun to his head and my father told him that if he didn't agree to let Johnny go, Luca would blow his brains out.'*

This is how Michael Corleone, youngest son of Don Vito Corleone, introduces his father's business to his girlfriend Kay Adams. His father is a gangster, a very important gangster. He is the Godfather of one of the most powerful and richest Mafia families in New York. His business is fear and murder. But he is a man you can trust.

Don Corleone has four children – Sonny, Fredo, Connie and Michael. But he is most proud of Michael. Michael is the cleverest of the four. He has been to college and fought bravely in World War II. The war has just finished as the story starts. Michael has no plans to join his father's business, and his father doesn't want him to. Michael keeps away as much as he can. He's different from the others in his family. He wants a quiet, peaceful and honest life with Kay.

But this isn't as easy as he thinks. Things happen, and Michael begins to change. He slowly realises that he is a Corleone too. Nothing is more important to him than his family. And he learns that he can be as deadly as the others.

American crime writer Mario Puzo was born in Manhattan, New York, in 1920. His family were poor Sicilians who came to America to look for work. They lived in an area of New York called Hell's Kitchen. Many New York gangsters lived here too. Today it is an expensive area. Puzo went to college in New York and then joined the army. During World War II he was sent to

Germany. He was not able to fight because of his poor eyesight, so he did office work. After the war, he became a journalist and writer, he heard many stories about the American Mafia as a reporter on the streets of New York. His first book, *The Dark Arena*, came out in 1955. It is about an American soldier who returns to Germany after the war. He always thought his next book, *The Fortunate Pilgrim* (1965), was his best book. It describes his Sicilian mother's honest and brave fight to bring up a family in New York. But it was his story of the Italian Mafia in New York that brought fortune to Puzo. *The Godfather* came out in 1969. Other Mafia books followed, including *The Sicilian* (1984) and *The Last Don* (1996). *The Sicilian* begins in 1952, at the point in *The Godfather* when Michael Corleone leaves Sicily and returns to America. Puzo also wrote the film stories for *Superman* and *Superman 2*. Mario Puzo was writing a story idea for a fourth Godfather film when he died in 1999.

In 1972 Hollywood film-maker Francis Ford Coppola began work on *The Godfather* films from Mario Puzo's book. He completed *The Godfather* in 1972 and *The Godfather 2* in 1974, but did not make *The Godfather 3* until 1990. Marlon Brando won an Oscar for his performance as Don Vito Corleone in the first *Godfather* film. Coppola and Puzo shared an Oscar for the writing of the film. In *The Godfather 2*, which goes back in time, the young Don Corleone is played by Robert de Niro.

Mario Puzo's *Godfather*, which takes place over the ten years from 1945 to 1955, is still the most famous story of the American Mafia. He invented the Corleone family by joining together characters from several real-life Mafia families. He borrowed from real dons to make Vito Corleone. He also said he used his mother for the non-violent parts of Vito's character. The singer

Johnny Fontane is said to be modelled on Frank Sinatra. Puzo introduced the Italian word 'consigliere' to the American public in his *Godfather* stories. A 'consigliere' is an adviser to the boss, and often his most trusted friend. He goes to important meetings with other families, sometimes in place of the boss. Like Tom Hagen in *The Godfather*, he is not always a blood member of the family.

The Mafia began in Sicily in the middle 1800s. It was a secret society outside the law. When Sicilians came to the East Coast of America in the late 1800s, they brought their Mafia ideas with them. A new organisation, the American Mafia, grew from this and is still strong today, especially in Chicago, New York and Philadelphia. Famous American Mafia bosses from the 1920s and 1930s include Al Capone in Chicago and Lucky Luciano in New York. The ideas behind the Mafia are complicated. Although it is a criminal organisation, it is built on strong family and Catholic values. Family members must be loyal, brave and respectful. As the story of *The Godfather* shows, it is also a very male world. Women are there to be mothers, to serve the men and not to ask questions.

The American Mafia is a popular subject in American entertainment – from the Chicago newspaper stories of Al Capone's violent murders in the 1920s to the very successful television story of the gangster family, *The Sopranos* (1999–2007) led by Godfather Anthony Soprano (James Gandolfini) and his wife Carmela Soprano (Edie Falco). Other Hollywood stories include Martin Scorsese's *Goodfellas* (1990), in which Ray Liotta plays gangster Henry Hill, and *Analyze This* (1999) with Robert de Niro. In the television show *The Simpsons*, Fat Tony is a regular character who runs the local Mafia. And *The Godfather: The Game* brought the Mafia up to date with its own computer game in 2006.

# Chapter 1   Wedding on Long Island

On the last Saturday in August, 1945, Miss Constanzia Corleone, daughter of Don Vito Corleone, married Carlo Rizzi. Her father had invited hundreds of people to the wedding at his huge house on Long Island, just outside New York. As the guests arrived, Don Corleone welcomed them all, rich and poor, with an equal show of love. Many of the guests had reason to be grateful to Don Corleone for their good luck in life, and they called him 'Godfather'★ to his face.

Standing next to him as he welcomed the guests were two of his three sons. Santino – or Sonny, as he was called – was the eldest. He was a tall, strong, good-looking man with thick brown hair. He looked uncomfortable in his white shirt and black suit. The second son, Fredo, was completely different. He was weak-looking and pale, with sad dark eyes and thin lips.

The youngest son, Michael, was sitting at a table in the corner of the garden with his girlfriend, Kay. There was a gentle, innocent quality to him, with his soft dark eyes and full lips, but his army uniform suggested that this was not a weak man. Just a quiet one. He was embarrassed by all the singing and dancing, but he was quietly pleased that Kay was enjoying herself. This was the first time that she had met his family.

'Who's that funny little fat man over there?' she asked, her eyes shining with excitement. 'He looks about sixty years old but he's dancing like a teenager.'

'That's Pete Clemenza,' Michael said. 'He's an old friend of my father's.'

---

★ Godfather: the head of an important family in the Mafia, which is a secret group of criminals. It is used here as a title of great respect.

'And what about him?' Kay looked at a large, ugly man who was sitting alone outside the house, talking to himself. 'He's very frightening.'

'That's Luca Brasi,' Michael smiled at Kay. 'He's waiting to speak to my father in private.'

'Yes, but who is he?'

'He helps my father sometimes,' Michael replied quietly, looking at his food.

Suddenly, the big man stood up and Kay looked away quickly, afraid that he was coming over to talk to her. But another man came up to the table instead. He had thin fair hair and blue eyes. Michael stood up and the two men hugged each other warmly.

'My brother, Tom Hagen, this is Kay Adams,' Michael finally said.

Tom Hagen shook Kay's hand, then whispered to Michael: 'My father wants to know why you don't go to see him.'

Michael sat down without speaking, and Tom walked away into the house, followed by Luca Brasi.

'If he's your brother, why does he have a different name?' Kay asked Michael when Tom had gone.

'When my brother Sonny was a boy,' Michael explained, 'he found Tom Hagen in the street. Tom had no home, so my father took him in and he's been with us ever since. He's a good lawyer. Not a Sicilian, but I think he's going to be a *Consigliere*.'

'What's that?'

'My father's chief adviser. Very important to the family.'

Suddenly, there came a loud, happy sound from the other side of the garden. The music and singing stopped. Connie, in her white wedding-dress, left her husband and ran towards the gate screaming: 'Johnny! Johnny!' She threw herself into the arms of a very handsome dark-haired man in a white suit, and covered his face with kisses. Then she led him by the hand through a crowd of excited, screaming girls, to meet her new husband, Carlo.

Kay turned to Michael excitedly. 'You didn't tell me your family knew Johnny Fontane,' she said.

'Sure. Do you want to meet him?' Michael smiled. 'My father helped him to become famous.'

'He did? How?'

At that moment, Johnny Fontane began to sing. 'Let's listen to the song,' Michael tried to change the subject.

'Please Michael,' Kay said impatiently, reaching across the table and squeezing his hand. 'Tell me.'

'Well, Johnny is my father's godson. When Johnny was beginning to become popular, he had a problem with his boss, a band-leader. Johnny wanted to leave the band, but this man wouldn't let him. So Johnny asked my father to help. My father went to see the band-leader and offered him $10,000 to let Johnny go. He said no. The next day my father went to see him with Luca Brasi. One hour later, the band-leader let Johnny go. For $1,000.'

Kay looked confused. 'How did he do that?'

'My father made him an offer he couldn't refuse. Luca held a gun to his head and my father told him that if he didn't agree to let Johnny go, Luca would blow his brains out.'

At first Kay didn't say anything. She thought Michael was joking. But Michael wasn't smiling. 'That's a true story, Kay,' he said quietly. Then he saw Kay beginning to look worried, a little frightened, so he squeezed her hand and added quickly: 'That's my family, Kay. That's not me.'

◆

'I don't know what to do, Godfather.' Johnny Fontane sat on the corner of the desk in Don Corleone's dark office and shook his head helplessly. Don Corleone was sitting in his leather chair, listening carefully to his favourite godson. He had, after all, travelled two thousand miles from California to be at his daughter's wedding. 'My voice is weak,' Johnny went on. 'I can't sing as well as I used to. There's a part in a film that I want. It would be perfect for me. If I had this part, I'd be a top star again. But the boss of the film company, Jack Woltz, won't give me the part. Can you help me?'

'Go and rest,' Don Corleone said. His voice was soft, but there was a rough quality to it that made everybody listen. It was a voice impossible to argue with. Something to do with the way he spoke without moving his mouth. 'In a month, this man will give you what you want.'

'Too late,' Johnny looked at his godfather unhappily. 'They start filming in a week.'

Don Corleone stood up and put a fatherly arm around Johnny's shoulder. 'I'm going to make this man an offer he can't refuse,' he said, leading Johnny towards the door. 'Now, go and enjoy yourself.' He kissed Johnny on the cheek, shut the door and turned to Tom Hagen, who had heard everything.

'What are we going to do with your daughter's new husband?' Tom asked. 'Shall we give him anything important to do?'

'No,' Don Corleone replied. 'Give him something small. A betting shop, maybe. But never discuss the family business with him.'

'Virgil Sollozzo called,' Tom went on. 'He wants to meet you next week.'

'We'll discuss that after you get back from California.'

Tom looked surprised. 'Why am I going to California?'

'I want you to help Johnny. You're going to talk to this Jack Woltz. I want you to go tonight. And now, if there's no other business, I'd like to go to my daughter's wedding.'

With these words, Don Corleone left Tom alone in the office, went outside, took his daughter by the hand and danced with her to the slow, Sicilian music.

*Don Corleone took his daughter by the hand and danced with her to the slow, Sicilian music.*

5

# Chapter 2    The Greatest Racehorse in the World

Tom Hagen arrived in Hollywood early the next morning. From the airport he went straight to his hotel, showered, shaved, and had breakfast. Then he drove to the film company for his meeting with Jack Woltz at ten o'clock.

Jack Woltz was giving a birthday party for one of his young girl stars in front of a lot of reporters. Tom waited patiently. Finally, Woltz walked up to him. He was a tall man with thick silver hair, expensive clothes and a hard, unfriendly face.

'OK, start talking,' he said to Tom. 'I'm a busy man.'

'I was sent by a friend of Johnny Fontane,' Tom said. 'He would be very grateful to you if you could do him a small favour.'

'I'm listening,' Woltz said, busily signing papers.

'Give Johnny the part in that new war film you're going to make.'

Woltz stopped writing and laughed. He took Tom by the arm, as if he was an old friend, and led him towards the door. 'And if I gave Johnny Fontane this part, what favour would your friend do for me?' he said.

'You have some problems with your workers,' Tom said. 'My friend could make these problems disappear. You also have a top star who's taking drugs . . .'

But Jack Woltz had heard enough. 'Listen to me!' he shouted angrily. 'You tell your boss, whoever he is, that Johnny Fontane will never get that film! You don't frighten me!'

'I'm a lawyer,' Tom said calmly. 'I'm not trying to frighten you.'

'I know all the lawyers in New York,' said Jack Woltz, 'but I've never heard of you. Who are you?'

'I work for one special family,' Tom said. 'Now, you have my number. I'll wait for your call.' He shook Woltz's hand and added, before leaving: 'By the way, I like your films very much.'

Tom was sure that, when Woltz realized who he worked for, he would call. And he was right. Late that afternoon, a car picked him up from the hotel and drove him out of the city to Jack Woltz's home in the country.

Woltz's house looked like something from a film. It was a huge pink-walled house surrounded by beautiful gardens, lakes and fields full of horses. Woltz welcomed Tom like an old friend, gave him a drink and showed him around.

'Why didn't you tell me you worked for Corleone, Tom?' he asked.

'I don't like to use his name unless it's really necessary.'

Woltz took Tom by the arm. 'Come with me, Tom,' he said. 'I want to show you something really beautiful.'

Woltz led Tom into a white building which was guarded by private detectives. Inside the building there were rows of horses. Woltz led Tom straight towards a beautiful horse with smooth black skin and a large, white, diamond-shaped mark between its eyes.

'You have an eye for beauty, don't you, Tom?' Woltz said proudly. 'This is Khartoum, the greatest racehorse in the world. I bought him in England for $600,000.' He looked lovingly into the animal's enormous dark eyes for a long time, talking to it softly like a lover, forgetting about Tom. Tom coughed with embarrassment. Woltz touched the horse one last time on the neck, then said to Tom: 'Let's go and have dinner.'

'Corleone is Johnny's godfather,' Tom began to explain at dinner. Although there were only two people at the table, the food was served by three waiters. 'To Italians, that's very important.'

'I respect that,' Woltz said. 'Just tell him he can ask me anything he likes. But not this. This is one favour I can't give him.'

'He never asks a second favour when the first one is refused.' Tom gave Woltz a warning look. 'Understood?'

This made Woltz angry. 'No,' he said, pointing his finger across the table at Tom. '*You* don't understand. Johnny Fontane never

7

gets that film. The part is perfect for him. It'd make him a big star. But I'm not going to give it to him. And do you know why?' He stood up and began to move slowly around the table towards Tom. 'I had a beautiful young actress. She was going to be a star. I spent hundreds of thousands of dollars on her, singing lessons, acting lessons, dancing lessons. Then Johnny Fontane came along and took her away from me. I lost her. He made me look stupid, and that's something I can never forgive. That's why I'll make sure that Johnny Fontane never works in films. Now, you get out of here! And if your boss wants to frighten me, tell him I'm no band-leader!'

Tom waited until Woltz had finished. 'Thank you for the dinner,' he said quietly. 'Could your car take me to the airport now, please? Mr Corleone is a man who likes to hear bad news immediately.'

Then without another word he left the table, took his hat from one of the servants and walked quickly out of the room.

♦

Jack Woltz was sleeping alone in his enormous bed. For some reason, this morning he woke up earlier than usual. The room was getting light. Everything was quiet. But he could feel that there was something wrong. He turned over and saw that there were wet red marks on his bedclothes. His night-shirt felt sticky, and there was a horrible smell in the room. He lifted the bedclothes off his body and looked down. His nightshirt was covered in blood. Without thinking, he sat up and pulled the bedclothes off his bed completely. The shock of what he saw nearly killed him. At first he couldn't breathe. He felt sick. Then, a moment later, he was filled with an animal fear. He opened his mouth and screamed.

For there, at the bottom of his bed, was the beautiful black head of his favourite racehorse, Khartoum. Somebody had cut it off during the night and put it in his bed while he was sleeping. It was stuck to the bed in a thick cake of blood, its mouth open, its huge round eyes staring at him like pieces of half-eaten fruit.

Jack Woltz's screams woke all the servants. Six hours later, Johnny Fontane received a phone call telling him that he had the part that he wanted in the film.

## Chapter 3   Virgil Sollozzo

Virgil Sollozzo was excellent at killing people with a knife. He was a strongly-built man with dark eyes and a wide, cruel mouth, but today he was trying to be polite and friendly. He had an important favour to ask, which was why he had asked for this meeting with Don Corleone.

'Don Corleone,' he smiled warmly. 'I need money to help me start a new business in drugs,' he said. 'If you give me one million dollars, I can promise you between three and four million dollars in your first year. After that, you'll get even more.'

Don Corleone said nothing at first. He seemed to be thinking. He looked around the room, at Sonny and Tom Hagen, and at Clemenza and Tessio, his two oldest friends. They were all watching him quietly with serious faces, waiting to hear his reply. Finally, he turned back to Sollozzo. 'Why do you come to me?' he asked in his usual rough whisper.

'I need a man who has important friends,' Sollozzo said, lowering his eyes respectfully towards the Don.

'And what about the Tattaglia family? How much will they get?'

Sollozzo looked surprised. He didn't know that Don Corleone had discovered that he worked with the Tattaglias. He nodded his congratulations in the direction of Tom Hagen, who had obviously done his homework, and turned back to Don

Corleone. 'Don't worry,' he said. 'I'll pay the Tattaglias from my own money.'

Don Corleone didn't reply. He stood up slowly, took a bottle from the table and politely offered Sollozzo some more wine. Sollozzo watched with a worried look as the Don sat down next to him.

Finally, Don Corleone spoke. 'I said that I would see you because I heard you were a serious man. You are a man I should respect. But I must refuse your offer. I will give you my reasons. It's true I have a lot of important friends in Government and the Law. But they wouldn't be my friends if they knew my business was drugs. Drugs is a dirty business.'

'But nobody will know,' Sollozzo said. 'I promise you the Tattaglias will make sure that nobody finds out.'

Don Corleone opened his mouth to reply but, before he could speak, Sonny said: 'Are you saying that the Tattaglias can promise that they'll . . .?'

He didn't finish his question. He saw a cold look in his father's eye and stopped talking at once. Don Corleone turned back to Sollozzo. 'I apologize for my children,' he said. 'They talk when they should listen. But Signor Sollozzo, my no is final. I congratulate you on your new business, and I wish you luck. Your business is different from mine. We mustn't be enemies. Thank you.'

Don Corleone got to his feet, and everybody stood up too. Sollozzo was angry, but he hid his feelings from the others. He politely shook Don Corleone's hand and walked out of the room.

Don Corleone waited for Tessio, Clemenza and Tom to leave the room, but called Sonny back. He stared up into his son's eyes for a moment, then said in an angry whisper: 'What's wrong with you? Has your brain gone soft?'

Sonny looked away, unable to look his father in the eye.

'I know you think this drugs business is a good idea. I know you think it's the business of the future, and I'm just a stupid old-fashioned man. But never tell anyone outside the family what you're thinking again.'

Sonny looked surprised at first, and then a little angry. But he was too afraid of his father to argue with him. He lowered his head respectfully, turned round and left the room.

Don Corleone immediately called Tom Hagen: 'Tell Luca Brasi to come in,' he said.

Brasi sat down alone in the office with Don Corleone. He had the terrible, frightening face of a killer, an enormous body that looked as if it was made of rock. But, as he looked at Don Corleone, his dark, unintelligent eyes were soft with respect. He loved his Godfather. And Don Corleone, knowing this, trusted Luca Brasi more than anyone he knew.

'I'm worried about Sollozzo,' Don Corleone said. 'I want you to find out what he's hiding, what he's got under his fingernails. Do you understand? Go to the Tattaglias. Pretend that you're not happy with our family and that you want to work for them. Then tell me what you find out.'

Luca Brasi asked no questions. He nodded once, lifted his mountainous body to its feet, and walked out of the room, proud to do whatever his Godfather asked him to do.

◆

For the next few weeks, Luca Brasi went regularly to the night-clubs controlled by the Tattaglia family. He made contact with Bruno Tattaglia, the youngest son and manager of the night-clubs. He told Bruno he was dissatisfied with the Corleone family. For a couple of months, nothing happened. Then one night, a few days before Christmas, Bruno told Luca he had a friend who wanted a private meeting with him.

'Who is he?' Luca wanted to know.

'Just a friend,' said Bruno. 'He wants to offer you something. Can you meet him here, after the club closes? Four o'clock tomorrow morning?'

Luca went back to his room and got ready. He thought for a moment about calling the Godfather to tell him about the meeting, but decided not to. Don Corleone never talked over the phone. As well as this, his job was completely secret. Not even Sonny or Tom Hagen knew what the Godfather had asked him to do. So he took out a gun, hid it under his jacket, lay on the bed and waited.

Luca arrived at the night-club just before four in the morning. The doorman had gone, but the door was open. Inside, the club was dark and empty, except for one man standing behind the bar. It was Bruno Tattaglia. Luca walked across to the bar and sat down. Bruno offered him a drink, but Luca shook his head. Moments later, a second man in a dark coat and grey hat moved out of the shadows and stood next to Bruno behind the bar.

'Do you know who I am?' he said in Italian, his face in shadow.

'I know you,' Luca replied. 'You're Sollozzo.'

'We need a man like you,' said Sollozzo. 'Strong and dangerous. I understand you're not happy with the Corleone family. Do you want to join me?'

'If the money's good.'

'$50,000 to start with.'

Luca nodded slowly, pretending to think.

Sollozzo held out his hand. 'Do you agree?'

Luca looked at Sollozzo's hand but he didn't take it. Instead he took out a cigarette and put it in his mouth. Bruno moved forward with a lighter. Luca rested his hands on the bar, bent forward and lit his cigarette. Bruno put the lighter in his pocket, smiled at Luca and gently touched the back of Luca's hand. Then suddenly, without warning, he took Luca's arm with his other

*A third man stepped out of the shadows behind him and threw a thin cord around Luca's thick neck. The cord pulled tight.*

hand and held it tight. At the same moment, Sollozzo pulled out a knife and pushed it straight through Luca's hand. Before Luca could move, a third man stepped out of the shadows behind him and threw a thin cord around his thick neck. The cord pulled tight. He tried to fight, but he couldn't get his hands up to the cord around his neck. They had planned everything perfectly. While Sollozzo and Bruno Tattaglia held one hand down, his other hand was pinned to the bar with the knife. The cord pulled tighter and tighter, cutting into his throat until he finally stopped moving and fell slowly to the floor. But Sollozzo, Tattaglia and the other man did not let him go for several more minutes. They needed to be sure that Luca Brasi, the most dangerous man in the Corleone family, was dead.

♦

Later on the same day, Tom Hagen came out of a large shop carrying Christmas presents for his children. Sollozzo was standing in the street, waiting for him.

'Happy Christmas, Tom,' Sollozzo smiled.

Tom nodded nervously.

'I'm glad I met you,' Sollozzo continued in a friendly voice. 'I want to talk to you.'

'I haven't got time,' Tom said, and began to walk away. But two men stepped forward and stopped him.

'Make time, *Consigliere*,' Sollozzo said, suddenly less friendly. 'Get in the car.' Then, noticing the look of fear in Tom's eyes, added quickly: 'Don't be frightened. If I wanted to kill you, you'd be dead already. Trust me.'

Without a word, Tom got into the car.

♦

Later that same afternoon, not knowing that Sollozzo had killed Luca Brasi and had kidnapped Tom Hagen, Don Corleone finished his work in the offices of his fruit company. He put on his coat and said to Fredo, who was reading a newspaper: 'Tell Paulie Gatto to bring the car. I want to go home.'

'I'll have to get it myself,' Fredo replied. 'Gatto's sick today.'

Don Corleone looked annoyed. 'That's the third time this month. Maybe we'd better get another man for the job.'

Fredo jumped to his feet. 'No, I'll get the car. It's OK,' he said. 'Paulie's a good boy. If he says he's sick, he's sick.'

Don Corleone waited inside the door until he saw Fredo park the car just outside. There was snow in the air and it was getting dark. He stepped on to the pavement and was about to get into the car when he decided to buy some fruit from the market on the other side of the street. He crossed the road and showed the fruit-seller the exact oranges and grapes that he wanted.

He was so busy choosing fruit that he didn't see two men in

black hats and long black coats turn the corner and walk quickly along the street towards him. He took the bag of fruit and paid the fruit-seller. Then he heard the sound of the two men running towards him. Without thinking, he dropped the bag of fruit and ran, surprisingly quickly for a man of his age, back across the street towards his car.

He had just reached the car when the two men pulled guns out of their coats and began to fire. Don Corleone was hit several times in the back. Fredo, on hearing the sound of guns, jumped out of the car; he was shaking so much with fear that he dropped his gun before he could use it. But his appearance was enough. On seeing him, the two men stopped shooting and ran away.

Fredo looked down and saw his father's body lying in a pool of blood. Unable to believe what had happened, he sat down in the road next to his father, pulled off his hat and began to cry like a baby.

## Chapter 4   Sicilian Message

Late that night, Michael and Kay were coming out of a theatre. Although they were staying in New York, Michael had told his family that he was in New Hampshire, over a hundred miles away. 'If I told my family we were in New York, we would have to see them right away,' he told Kay. 'Then we wouldn't be able to be alone together.'

The night was freezing, and Michael and Kay held each other closely as they walked slowly along the crowded pavement.

'What do you want for Christmas?' he asked Kay.

Kay laughed and kissed his frozen cheek. 'Just you,' she said.

They walked a little further, then suddenly Kay stopped. 'Mike,' she said, looking behind her, her face white with shock.

'What's the matter?' said Mike, confused.

She took his hand and led him back to a newspaper shop they had just passed. She pointed to a newspaper. Michael picked it up. 'VITO CORLEONE SHOT FIVE TIMES' he read on the front page. Opening it, he saw a photograph of his father. 'KILLERS SHOOT UNDERWORLD BOSS'.

Without looking at Kay, he ran across the street to a public telephone and rang Sonny.

'Sonny?' he said. 'It's Michael. Is he all right?'

'We don't know yet, but he's hit bad, Mikey,' his brother said. 'Where have you been? We've been worried.'

Michael suddenly felt guilty about lying to his family about New Hampshire. 'I called. Didn't Tom tell you?'

'No. But come home, Mikey. You should be with Mama. We need you.'

*Michael picked up the newspaper. 'VITO CORLEONE SHOT FIVE TIMES' he read on the front page.*

Michael put down the phone. Kay, who had followed him across the road, looked at him with tears in her eyes. Michael kissed her and hugged her tightly. Then, stepping away from her, he said: 'Go back to the hotel, Kay. I've got to go home.'

♦

As soon as Sonny had put down the phone, there was a knock on the door.

'They say he's dead, Sonny,' said Pete Clemenza as he came in.

Sonny took him roughly by the collar and threw him against the wall.

'Take it easy,' Clemenza cried.

Sonny took a deep breath and took his hands away. 'I'm sorry,' he said. And then asked: 'How's Paulie?'

'Paulie wasn't there. He was sick.'

'What do you mean? How many times has he been sick?'

'I don't know, Sonny,' Clemenza said, half afraid, half confused. 'Three, maybe four times.'

'Listen. I don't care how sick he is. I want you to bring him to my father's house now. Do you understand?'

After Clemenza had gone, Sonny looked at his wife, who was standing nervously in the doorway, holding a crying baby. He hugged and kissed them both, trying to calm them down. Trying to calm himself down. Suddenly, the phone rang again. The voice on the other end was very soft, very gentle:

'We have Tom Hagen,' the voice said. 'In about three hours we'll let him go. He'll have a message for you. Don't do anything stupid until you've heard what he has to say. Your father's dead. Let's all keep clear-headed about this, OK?'

'OK.' Although he felt like shouting, Sonny spoke quietly. 'I'll wait.'

He immediately left his house and crossed the private road to the one where his father lived. He found his mother in the kitchen.

'Papa's hurt,' he told her. 'I don't know how bad.'

His mother just said: 'I'll go and get ready. I might be able to see him.' She didn't ask her son any questions. A Sicilian woman was taught never to ask men questions.

Sonny took a mouthful of bread, went into his father's office and picked up the phone. 'Tessio? I want fifty good men here right away.'

'What about Clemenza's people?' Tessio asked.

'No. I don't want to use his men right now.'

Then he made a second call. This time it was to a friend of his who worked for the telephone company. 'Farrell? I want you to do me a favour. I want you to check two phone numbers for me. Give me all the calls they made and received over the last three months. It's very important. Give me the information before midnight.' He gave him Paulie Gatto's and Pete Clemenza's numbers.

Then he made a third call. He phoned Luca Brasi. But this time there was no answer.

♦

When Michael arrived, he found his father's house full of men he didn't know. He went into the living-room, shook hands with a sad-looking Pete Clemenza, kissed Tom Hagen's wife on the cheek, then went into his father's corner-room office.

Sonny was sitting with Tessio, talking quietly. When he saw Michael, he stood up and ran towards him. 'I'm really glad to see you,' he said, hugging his brother warmly. 'Mama's at the hospital with the old man. He's going to be OK, thank God.' But then he saw Michael sit down, and he stopped smiling. 'What are you doing?' he said. 'I'm talking important business with Tessio.'

'Maybe I can help,' Michael said.

'If you stay here, you'll hear things you shouldn't,' Sonny warned him. 'The old man will kill me if he finds out.'

*'If you stay here, you'll hear things you shouldn't,'*
*Sonny warned him.*

Michael stared at his brother. 'He's my father too,' he said quietly.

'OK,' said Sonny, annoyed at Michael's refusal to leave. 'You want to hear? Then I'll tell you. Whose head do we shoot off, Paulie's or Clemenza's? One of them betrayed the old man to Sollozzo. Who do you think it was?'

If Sonny was hoping to shock Michael, he didn't succeed. His younger brother just looked at him coldly and said: 'Not Clemenza.'

Sonny stared at his brother for a moment, then looked at Tessio with disbelief. 'I don't believe it. The college boy's right. It *was* Paulie. I had their numbers checked. While Paulie was sick, he got phone calls from Sollozzo's people.'

Michael got up and stood in front of his brother. 'Is there going to be a war, Sonny?' he said.

'Of course there is. Unless the old man tells me different. Sollozzo's a dead man. I'm going to hit all five families if I have to. The Tattaglias are going to eat dirt.'

'Wait, Sonny,' Michael said with a look of warning in his eyes. 'This isn't how Papa would do it.'

Just then, they heard loud voices from outside the door, and the sound of people laughing. Sonny, Michael and Tessio rushed out of the room and saw Tom Hagen standing at the front door, hugging his wife and smiling.

♦

Sonny, Tom, Clemenza and Tessio sat in the Godfather's office, talking. They were planning to kill Sollozzo, wondering where Luca Brasi was, thinking about what to do if the Godfather died. Michael sat by the desk, listening to the conversation, but not permitted to speak. There was a knock at the door, and Paulie Gatto came in. He was blowing his nose, and looked very ill.

'There's a man at the gate,' Paulie said, looking at Sonny. 'He's got something for you.'

Sonny sent Tessio out to see what it was. Then he smiled at Paulie. 'Are you OK, Paulie?' he asked. 'Why don't you go to the kitchen and get something to drink? You look terrible.'

When Paulie had gone, Sonny turned to Clemenza. 'I want you to kill him tomorrow,' he said. 'He betrayed the old man to Sollozzo. I don't want to see him again.'

Clemenza hid his surprise and just nodded. To him, it was just a job.

Then Tessio came into the room. He was carrying something inside a large piece of brown paper. He gave it to Sonny, and stepped back. Sonny opened the paper. Inside, there was Luca Brasi's jacket. And inside the jacket, there was a dead fish. Sonny looked up at Tessio, confused. 'What's this?' he asked.

'It's a Sicilian message,' Tessio said in his deep but strangely gentle voice. 'It means that Luca Brasi sleeps with the fishes.'

## Chapter 5    Seeds of Revenge

The next night, before going to visit his father in hospital, Michael had dinner with Kay in the hotel. They didn't talk much. Kay kept looking across the table at him, worried by his silence. Finally, he put down his glass of wine, stood up and said: 'I have to go.'

'Can I come with you?' Kay said, staring at her food.

'There'll be policemen at the hospital,' Michael said, putting on his coat. 'Reporters too. I don't want to get you mixed up in this.'

Kay looked at him sadly. She understood that, since the shooting of his father, he was different. He was more distant from her. 'When will I see you again?' she asked quietly.

Michael found it difficult to look her in the eyes. 'Go back to your parents and I'll call you,' he said.

But Kay repeated her question: 'When will I see you again?'

This time, Michael looked at her. 'I don't know,' he said, touching her gently on the shoulder. Then, without another word, he left her sitting alone at the table and walked towards the door.

♦

When Michael got out of the taxi, he was surprised to see that the street outside the hospital was quiet and empty. When he climbed the steps and went through the front door, he was even more surprised to find that there was nobody inside the hospital either. 'Where are Tessio's and Clemenza's men?' he thought nervously as he took the lift up to the fourth floor.

There was nobody outside his father's room. Michael opened

the door slowly and walked inside. His father was lying in bed; glass bottles hung next to him. As Michael stood by the bed and looked down at his sleeping father, he heard a noise behind him in the doorway.

He turned quickly. It was only a nurse.

'What are you doing here?' she whispered angrily.

'I'm Michael Corleone. This is my father. There's nobody here. What happened to the guards?'

'Your father had too many visitors. The police came and made them all leave ten minutes ago.'

Michael thought quickly. He picked up the phone by the bed and told Sonny to send some people to the hospital at once. Then he told the nurse to help him move his father's bed to another room. When she complained, he said: 'You know my father? Men are coming here to kill him. You understand? Now help me, please.'

As Michael and the nurse were pushing the bed carefully through the narrow door of another room, they heard the sound of someone coming up the stairs. Michael closed the door quietly and looked through the window. He saw a man in a black hat and long black coat carrying flowers. Michael didn't know who he was, but decided that he didn't look like a killer.

'Who are you?' he said, opening the door.

The man turned round, surprised. 'I am Enzo,' he said. 'The butcher.'

'Listen, Enzo,' Michael said. 'You'd better get out of here. There's going to be trouble.'

Enzo lifted his head and looked at Michael proudly. 'If there is trouble, I stay here to help you. For your father.'

Michael didn't argue. He needed help. 'Go outside,' he told Enzo, 'and stand in front of the hospital. I'll be out in a minute.'

He went back into the dark room and looked down at his

father. 'It's all right, Papa,' he whispered, softly touching his father's grey hair. 'I'll take care of you now.' He bent down to kiss his father's hand and, when he looked up, he saw a tear in the corner of his father's eye.

Michael found Enzo outside on the steps in front of the hospital. He threw Enzo's flowers away, turned up the collar of Enzo's coat and told him to put his hand in his pocket as if he had a gun. They waited nervously in the icy cold and dark.

A few minutes later, the silence was broken by the soft sound of an engine moving slowly along the street. Michael and Enzo held their breath as a long black car appeared in front of the hospital gates and stopped. Shadowy shapes of men in hats moved inside the car. They seemed to be talking to each other. Then the car moved quickly away.

Michael smiled at Enzo. 'You did well,' he said.

Enzo smiled and took out a packet of cigarettes, but his hands were shaking. Michael lit a cigarette for him. To his surprise, his own hands weren't shaking at all. He felt completely calm.

Suddenly, there was the sound of police cars, and the street outside the hospital was filled with policemen.

'Good old Sonny,' Michael smiled as he walked down the steps to meet them. What happened next took him completely by surprise. Two policemen took him roughly by the arms while a third policeman searched him. A huge police captain with a strong red face and white hair walked towards him.

'I thought I locked all you gangsters up,' he said angrily to Michael. 'Who are you?'

Michael looked up into the police captain's fiery eyes and said, unafraid: 'What happened to the men guarding my father, captain?'

'You little animal!' the captain shouted. 'Don't tell me my business! Now, get out of here and stay away from this hospital!'

The policemen let go of Michael's arms, but Michael didn't

move. 'I'm not going until you put some guards outside my father's room,' he said.

The captain shouted to his men: 'Take him away!'

Michael stared at him coldly. 'What's Sollozzo paying you to betray my father, captain?'

At this, the captain lost all control. 'Hold his arms!' he told the policemen behind Michael. Then, as they held him, he hit Michael hard in the face.

Before he could hit Michael again, another car suddenly arrived. It was Tom Hagen with a group of men to guard the Godfather. Tom saw Michael's face covered in blood and said: 'Do you want to report this?'

Michael had trouble talking, but he managed to say: 'That's OK, Tom. It was an accident.' As he spoke, he didn't take his eyes off the police captain. He tried to smile. He didn't want to show anyone how he really felt at that moment. Seeds of revenge were growing in his icy heart.


## Chapter 6   Nothing Personal

The entrance to the private road where the Corleone family lived was crowded with cars and men with guns. As Michael and Clemenza got out of the car together and walked in, Tessio came to meet them.

'Why all the guns?' Clemenza asked.

'We'll need them,' Tessio said. 'After Sollozzo tried to kill the Don at the hospital, Sonny got angry. We killed Bruno Tattaglia at four o'clock this morning.'

Inside the house, Sonny was in an excited, happy mood. He held Michael's badly bruised face in his hands and laughed. 'Hey Mikey, you look beautiful!'

Michael pushed his brother's hands away and went to pour

himself a drink to take away the pain.

'Hey, Tom,' Sonny said, turning to the *Consigliere*. 'Listen to this. Sollozzo wants to talk. He wants us to send Michael to hear his offer.'

Tom looked worried. Sonny was talking and laughing as if it was all a joke. 'Perhaps we should hear what Sollozzo has to say,' he said, 'We don't want another war.'

Sonny stopped smiling at once. 'No!' he said, suddenly angry. 'No more. Not this time. No more meetings. No more Sollozzo tricks. I want Sollozzo dead. If not, we'll have a war!'

'You're taking things too personally,' Tom said, getting angry too. 'This is business.'

'I don't want your advice,' Sonny said. 'I just want you to help me win, all right?'

When everybody had calmed down, Tom explained to Sonny why he thought killing Sollozzo was a bad idea. 'Sollozzo's paying the police captain who hit Michael a lot of money. His name's McCluskey. He's agreed to be Sollozzo's bodyguard at the meeting. Now you must understand, Sonny, that you can't kill Sollozzo while he's with McCluskey. Nobody's ever shot a New York police captain. It would be a disaster. All the five families would come after you. All our important friends would disappear. We'd have no friends in the world. We'd be finished!'

Sonny listened to Tom carefully, and finally agreed to wait. But Michael, who had heard the whole conversation from his armchair said: 'We can't wait.'

Sonny and Tom stared at him in surprise, but Michael went on thoughtfully: 'We've got to kill Sollozzo before he kills Papa.'

Tom thought for a moment, and then said quietly: 'Mike's right.'

'But you just told me we can't kill him because of McCluskey!' Sonny said, waving one arm angrily at Tom.

'They want to have a meeting, right?' Michael began to take

control of the conversation. 'Find out where it's going to be. If Clemenza can think of a way of hiding a gun there, I'll kill them both.'

There was a long silence as everybody looked at each other in disbelief at what they had heard Michael say. Then Clemenza laughed, closely followed by Sonny and Tessio. Only Tom looked serious. He knew that Michael wasn't joking.

'Hey,' Sonny laughed, walking up and down in front of Michael, who sat strangely still in his armchair looking straight in front of him. 'What are you going to do? Nice college boy. You want to kill a police captain because he hit you in the face? This is business. You're taking it too personally.'

Tom smiled to himself. He had used those exact words to Sonny minutes earlier.

Michael became angry. 'This is a policeman who's mixed up in drugs. He's dishonest.' He turned to Tom. 'Listen, if he's killed, our friends in the newspapers will make a good story out of it. Isn't that true, Tom?'

Tom looked at Michael thoughtfully for a second before saying: 'You might be right.'

'All right, all right!' Sonny held up his hands. He gave Michael a long, hard look, then shook his head as if he didn't want to hear what he was saying. 'OK, we'll do it. Clemenza will teach you everything you need to know. We'll take care of everything. When it's over, things'll be very bad, but that'll be our problem. You'll be out of it, Mikey. We'll make you disappear for a nice long holiday until things calm down.' He looked at Michael, and added in a quiet voice filled with respect for his younger brother: 'You can do it, Mikey. I know you can.'

Michael smiled. He was beginning to feel a real Corleone at last. 'I learnt things from my father too,' he said.

♦

Eventually, after a lot of nervous preparation, the meeting between Michael and Sollozzo was arranged. At the last minute, Sonny was able to discover where it was going to take place: a small family restaurant in the Bronx★ called 'Louie's'.

Michael waited alone, as agreed with Sollozzo, outside Dempsey's restaurant on Broadway.† Finally, a large black car stopped in front of him, and Michael got into the passenger seat. In the back seat sat Sollozzo and Captain McCluskey, although this evening the policeman was not in uniform.

Sollozzo put a friendly hand on Michael's shoulder and said: 'I'm glad you came, Mike. We're going to solve all our problems tonight.'

'I don't want anyone to try to hurt my father again,' Michael replied in a quiet, cold voice.

'Don't worry,' Sollozzo said warmly. 'He'll be safe. I promise. But please keep an open mind when we talk. I hope you're not a hothead like your brother, Sonny. You can't talk business with him.'

Just then, McCluskey moved forward in his seat and offered Michael his hand. 'You're a good boy,' he said in a strong, friendly voice. 'I'm sorry about the other night, Mike. Nothing personal, I hope. I'm getting too old for my job, I guess.'

Without turning round, Michael shook the policeman's hand over his shoulder.

'And now I'm afraid I've got to search you,' McCluskey said. 'So turn round please, on your knees . . .'

Michael did as he was asked. 'He's clean,' McCluskey said at last, sitting back next to Sollozzo. Michael slowly put his hat back on his head, and stared out of the window with a dead look in his eyes.

★ The Bronx: an area of New York City, north-east of Manhattan Island, which is the most famous part of the city.
† Broadway: a large street in Manhattan, famous for its theatres, night-clubs and restaurants.

Half an hour later, McCluskey, Sollozzo and Michael were sitting at a small round table in the middle of a quiet restaurant.

'How's the Italian food here?' McCluskey asked Sollozzo with real interest.

'Good,' Sollozzo replied. 'The best in the city.'

When the waiter had poured wine into their glasses, Sollozzo began to talk to Michael in Italian. 'I have great respect for your father,' he said. 'What happened between him and me is just business. His thinking is old-fashioned. Let's forget these disagreements. I want peace.'

Michael tried to reply in Italian, but he couldn't think of the words. So he spoke English instead. 'You must promise me that no one will try to kill my father again.'

Sollozzo looked at Michael in wide-eyed innocence. 'You think too much of me,' he said. 'I'm the one in danger, not your father. I'm not as clever as you think. All I want is peace.'

Michael looked at McCluskey. The policeman seemed more interested in his food than the conversation. He turned back to Sollozzo, thought for a moment, then said: 'I have to go to the bathroom. Is that OK?'

'No problem,' said McCluskey.

But Sollozzo didn't like it. When Michael stood up, he stopped him and searched him very carefully. Finally satisfied that Michael wasn't carrying a gun, he sat down again. 'Don't take too long,' he said, staring at Michael moodily.

Michael found the gun hidden in the toilet. Clemenza had done his job well. He pushed the gun into the top of his trousers, buttoned his jacket, took a few deep breaths to calm himself down, and returned to the restaurant.

Sollozzo was sitting with his back to him, smoking a cigarette. McCluskey looked at Michael out of the corner of his eye, but went on eating. Sollozzo turned round. Michael walked back to his chair and sat down. Sollozzo began talking again in Italian, but Michael couldn't understand a word. He wasn't listening. All he could hear was the sound of his heart, the thunder of blood between his ears. Somewhere behind the restaurant there was the sound of a train. It was getting louder. McCluskey went on eating greedily. Sollozzo moved his face closer to Michael's to talk above the noise of the train. Now was the moment. Now!

Michael jumped to his feet, pulled the gun from his trousers, pointed it straight at Sollozzo's head and fired. The bullet hit Sollozzo between the eyes. McCluskey stared at Sollozzo in surprise, as if watching something far away. He did not seem to realize his own danger. His fork was half-way to his mouth. He was just beginning to understand what was happening when Michael fired at him. The shot was bad. It hit McCluskey in the throat. He dropped his fork, put his hands to his neck and began to cough up food and blood. Very carefully, very coolly, Michael fired the next bullet straight into the policeman's brain. McCluskey stared at Michael for a second then fell forward, his head hitting the table with a crash.

Michael turned away. He let the gun fall from his hand and, looking straight in front of him, he walked quickly out of the restaurant, round the corner and into the car where Tessio was waiting to drive him away.

## Chapter 7   Apollonia

After the shooting of Captain McCluskey, the police took revenge on all five New York families. The Five Families War of 1946 had begun. But Michael wasn't there. He was hiding thousands of miles away, in Sicily.

He was staying with Don Tommasino, a friend of his father's and a Godfather himself. In the evenings, Michael sat in a huge garden filled with flowers, drinking wine and hearing old stories

*McCluskey's fork was half-way to his mouth when Michael fired at him.*

about his family. During the day, he walked in the Sicilian countryside, dressed in old clothes. Two bodyguards, Fabrizio and Calo, went everywhere with him, carrying guns over their shoulders. Michael often thought of Kay during these long walks in the white hot sun. He felt sad and guilty that he had left America without saying goodbye to her.

One morning, seven months after arriving in Sicily, Michael decided to walk into the mountains past the hilltop town of Corleone. He walked with his two bodyguards along dusty country roads, past fruit-trees and fields of flowers. The hot, still air was rich with the smell of oranges. Along the way, they met a group of girls and children picking flowers. They stopped to watch them pass. One girl in a simple dress with a basket over her arm stopped in front of Michael to pick a small pink flower. Michael watched her, studying the way that her long, brown hair shone in the sunlight and hung around her face. Suddenly, the girl lifted her head and looked at him. She had large brown eyes, and her heart-shaped mouth was red with the juice of grapes. Michael felt weak, as if hit by lightning. He had never seen anyone so lovely.

The girl lowered her eyes with a shy smile, ran back to join her friends and disappeared down the road. Fabrizio noticed the look on Michael's face and laughed. 'Let's go and find out who she is,' he suggested. Michael agreed, and followed Fabrizio and Calo down a narrow path towards the village where the girls and children had gone.

In the village, they sat at a table outside a small café. The owner of the café was a short man with white hair and a dark moustache. He smiled as he served them, not worried at all by the fact that his customers carried guns. This was not unusual in Sicily.

When Fabrizio asked the café owner about the beautiful girl they had seen picking flowers, and described her to him, a strange thing happened. The man stopped smiling, looked at the three men angrily, and disappeared inside the café. Fabrizio followed him inside and, moments later, ran out looking nervous.

'Quick, we must go,' he said to Michael. 'He's really angry. The girl's his daughter.'

But Michael didn't move. He stared at Fabrizio and said: 'I want to speak to him.'

Fabrizio quickly drank some wine, picked up his gun and went inside to bring the man to Michael. The café owner appeared with two young, strong-looking men at his side. They were his sons. He looked down at Michael without speaking, a hard look in his eye.

Michael spoke to him quietly. 'I'm sorry if I made you angry,' he said. 'I'm an American hiding in Sicily. My name's Michael. You can tell the police, and make a lot of money. But then your daughter would lose a father instead of getting a husband. With your agreement, I would like to meet your daughter. With all respect.'

The café owner's face softened. He looked with interest at Michael, this young man with the strange mixture of softness and confidence in his voice. He noticed that the two men with guns looked at this young man with great respect. He was obviously important, and probably rich.

'Come on Sunday afternoon,' he said. 'My name is Vitelli and my house is up there in the hills, above the village.'

'And what's you daughter's name?' Michael said, standing up and shaking the man's hand.

'Apollonia,' the café owner smiled.

◆

That Sunday, Michael, dressed in his best clothes, brought presents for Apollonia and all her family. He gave Apollonia some jewellery. He began to visit the family home regularly after that.

One evening, at the dinner table, he noticed that she was wearing the jewellery he had given her. It was her way of saying that she liked him. He invited her for a walk in the country, and she agreed. They walked side by side, but they were careful not to touch each other. They were not alone. All the women in Apollonia's family walked behind them, followed by Calo and Fabrizio, carrying their guns.

Two weeks later, Michael and Apollonia got married. Compared to his sister's wedding to Carlo in New York two years earlier, it was a simple Sicilian wedding. Apollonia wore white while all the other women wore black. The villagers stood in the streets and threw flowers as the couple passed on foot from the church to Apollonia's house in the hills. The wedding guests walked behind the couple and, behind the guests, there was a band of musicians. The wedding party went on until midnight. Then Michael took Apollonia away, and drove her to Don Tommasino's house outside Corleone.

*It was a simple Sicilian wedding.*

# Chapter 8   A Bridge Too Far

Two years after their wedding, Connie and Carlo Rizzi were not happily married. Carlo drank a lot and saw other women. Connie shouted at him all the time, and Carlo used to hit her. One day, Sonny visited his sister and saw her face was covered in bruises. He became very angry and, although Connie tried to stop him, he rushed away to find Carlo.

He found Carlo sitting outside the betting shop where he worked. Sonny jumped out of his car and ran quickly towards him. Carlo tried to escape, but Sonny dived and caught him by the ankles, pulling him down with a crash. Then, while Carlo was still on the ground, Sonny kicked and hit him, screaming at him all the time. Carlo didn't try to fight. He stayed on his knees and covered his head with his hands. Finally, Sonny grew tired. He looked down at Carlo's bruised and bloody body and said: 'If you ever touch my sister again, I'll kill you!'

A few weeks later, the telephone rang in the kitchen of Don Corleone's house. Sonny was called to the phone. It was Connie, and she was crying. Carlo had hit her badly, and she wanted to come home.

As he listened, Sonny's face went red and he began to shake. 'I'm coming right over,' he told his sister. 'Just wait there.'

'Please Sonny, don't . . .' Connie began, but Sonny put down the phone and ran straight out of the house.

Tom Hagen tried to stop him, but Sonny refused to listen. As Sonny drove quickly out of the gates, Tom told two bodyguards to follow him.

Between Long Island and the City of New York, there was a kind of bridge. Before anyone could cross, they had to stop at the tollbooth and pay. When Sonny arrived at the bridge, only one tollbooth was open. He had to wait because another car was in front of him. Sonny impatiently looked for some money in his jacket pocket. The car in front of Sonny drove forward a little way and stopped. Sonny drove up to the tollbooth. He gave the man inside his money and tried to drive away, but the car was still in front of him. The man in the tollbooth dropped the money and bent down to pick it up. From the corner of his eye, Sonny noticed something moving in the empty tollbooth on his right. He looked round and saw four men standing in the windows looking at him. At the same moment, two men got out of the car in front and began to walk towards him. They were carrying machine-guns. Sonny thought about driving backwards, but he was too late. In the second before anything happened, Sonny knew that he was a dead man.

There was a sudden thunder of noise, and bullets crashed through the windows of his car from all directions. Before Sonny could dive for cover, he was hit several times in the chest and head. But he was a strong man. He refused to die quietly. He pulled himself across the seat, opened the door and half jumped, half fell out of the car. He tried to pull his gun from his jacket, but bullets continued to hit him. At last, with a wild and angry look on his face, he fell to the ground in a pool of blood and stopped moving.

By the time the bodyguards that Tom had sent to follow him arrived, Sonny Corleone, eldest son of Vito Corleone, was dead, and his killers were gone.

♦

Later that night, Tom Hagen sat alone in Don Corleone's dark office, drinking. He couldn't believe that Sonny was dead. He heard the door behind him open and close. Turning round, he saw Don Corleone.

He looked very old and tired as he walked stiffly across the room. He had lost weight, and his clothes hung loosely from his body.

'Give me some wine,' he said as he lowered himself slowly into his favourite leather armchair. He waited while Tom poured him a drink, then half spoke, half whispered: 'My wife was crying before she fell asleep. Outside my window, I saw Tessio and Clemenza coming to the house and it's midnight. So, Tom, I think you should tell your Don what everybody already knows.'

'I was about to come up and tell you,' Tom said.

'But you needed a drink first.'

'Yes,' Tom looked down, ashamed.

'You've had your drink. You can tell me now.'

Tom looked up, his eyes filled with tears. 'They shot Sonny,' he said, his voice shaking. 'He's dead.'

Don Corleone closed his eyes. For a second he, too, seemed about to cry. But when he opened his eyes again, they were dry. 'I want no revenge,' he said sadly. 'I want you to arrange a meeting with the heads of the five families. This war stops now.'

## Chapter 9  A Good American Wife

In the first weeks of married life, Michael and Apollonia went for walks in the hills and drove around the countryside in their small black car. But news of the wedding had reached Michael's enemies. Don Tommasino told Michael that it was too dangerous for him to leave the house. He put men with guns around the house to guard him, and told Fabrizio and Calo to stay with Michael all the time. Although he was a prisoner in his home, Michael wasn't too unhappy. He had Apollonia. He spent the time teaching her how to speak English and how to drive the car.

One morning, Don Tommasino came home to tell Michael that Sonny was dead. It wasn't safe for Michael to stay in the house any more. He had found a safe house outside Syracuse, and he would have to leave at once. Apollonia could live with her parents for a short time. She could join him later.

The next morning, Michael stood at his bedroom window and saw Fabrizio sitting in a garden chair.

'Get the car,' Michael called down. 'I'm leaving in five minutes.'

'Is your wife coming with you?' Fabrizio asked.

'No, I want you to take her to her father's house until I'm safe.'

Michael washed, then went downstairs to the kitchen, where he found Calo having breakfast.

'Where's Apollonia?' Michael asked.

'She's in the car,' Calo said, his mouth full of bread. 'You'll get a surprise. She's driving it alone. She'll make a good American wife.'

Michael smiled and went outside. Apollonia was sitting in the car, her hands on the wheel. She laughed and waved at him. But Michael was annoyed to see Fabrizio about to disappear through the garden gates.

'Fabrizio. Where are you going?' Michael called.

Fabrizio looked over his shoulder at Michael, then continued to walk quickly away. Michael watched him go, confused at first. Then he looked at the car. Suddenly, without thinking, he realized there was danger.

He shouted to Apollonia: 'No! No!' But she never heard him. There was a loud explosion and Michael was thrown to the ground. When he looked up, pieces of burning car were lying all over the garden. The bomb, which someone had intended for him, had killed his beautiful, innocent wife instead.

## Chapter 10    No Revenge

The secret meeting between the heads of the five New York families and all the other important families in America took place in a large room above a bank. Everybody sat around a large table, each head with his *Consigliere* sitting close behind. Don Corleone, who had invited them all, was the first to stand up and speak.

'How did things get so far?' he said. 'It's so unnecessary.' He looked at the small man with dark, oily hair and shadows under his eyes who was sitting opposite him. 'Tattaglia, you've lost a son. I've lost a son too. Why can't we stop this foolish war now before more people die?'

A handsome man with silver hair who sat at one end of the table began to speak. This was Barzini. 'We all know Don Corleone is an honest man,' he said. 'We can trust him.'

'Yes,' Tattaglia said to Barzini. 'He has many important friends. But he refused to share them with us.'

'I only ever refused to help you once,' Don Corleone looked at Tattaglia. He was thinking about the meeting with Sollozzo. 'I refused to help you because I don't like the drugs business.'

'Times have changed,' Barzini said. 'A man who refuses to help his friends is not a true friend. Don Corleone must share his important friends in Law and Government with us. We will pay him well for his help, of course.'

The Godfathers talked for a long time. Finally Don Corleone said: 'I'm a man you can trust. I'll do whatever I can for peace.'

'Then we all agree,' Barzini smiled. 'The drugs business will be permitted, but controlled. And Don Corleone will share his important friends with us.'

'If Don Corleone promises not to take revenge on us for his son's death,' Tattaglia said.

Don Corleone looked sadly at Tattaglia. 'Is revenge going to bring your son back to you? Or my boy to me? I promise, there will be no revenge. But only if my youngest son is permitted to come back safely. He has had to live abroad since that Sollozzo business. I want him home. But I warn you, if anything happens to my son – if he mysteriously falls off the boat on his way home, or if he's hit by lightning after he returns – then I will blame some of the people in this room. That, I will not forgive. But if my son is permitted to return safely to New York, then I promise

I will not be the one to break the peace we have made here today.'

At this, he stood up and opened his arms to Tattaglia. Tattaglia stood up too, and the two men walked around the table. They met behind Barzini's chair and hugged each other warmly. Then all the Godfathers in the room stood up and began to hug and kiss each other, congratulating each other on the end of the war.

## Chapter 11    Ghost from the Past

One autumn afternoon, as Kay was walking home, she saw a large black car parked outside the school where she was a teacher. Next to the car, there was a serious-looking man in a black hat and long black coat, watching her. Kay stopped as if she had seen a ghost.

'Michael,' she said. 'How long have you been back?'

'About a year,' he said quietly. Then, walking slowly towards her, he said: 'It's good to see you Kay.'

They walked together through the park, hands in pockets, a little shy with each other after so much time. 'I'm working for my father now,' Michael explained. 'He's been sick. Very sick.'

'But you're not like him,' Kay replied. 'I thought you weren't going to become a man like your father.'

'As I've grown older, I've learnt to respect him more. He's just an ordinary man who loves his family, that's all.'

'Ordinary men don't have other men killed,' Kay said.

'Listen, Kay,' Michael stopped walking and looked her in the eyes. 'In five years' time, my family will have no more problems. We'll be a lawful, respectable family. Trust me. That's all I can tell you about my business.'

Kay's eyes filled with tears. 'Michael, why did you come here?' she said. 'What do you want with me after all this time? You didn't call. You didn't write . . .'

'I came here because I need you. I care for you.'

'Please stop it.'

But Michael went on: 'Because I want you to marry me.'

Kay shook her head. 'It's too late.'

'I promise I'll do anything you ask,' Michael continued in a soft, calm voice. 'Let's forget the last two years. What's important is that we have each other. That we have children. Kay, I need you. And I love you.'

As Michael was speaking, Kay kept looking away. She didn't know what to say. Michael had changed. He was different now. There was something cold about him, something hard . . .

But in the end, this didn't matter. Before she could answer him, the large black car drove up and stopped next to them. Michael opened the back door for her and waited. In her heart, Kay realized that she still loved him. Without a word, she stepped inside the car.

## Chapter 12   Many Changes

As months turned into years, there were many changes. Michael and Kay got married and had two children. Connie and Carlo Rizzi moved with their children into a house on Long Island, to be near the rest of the family. Fredo was sent to Las Vegas, where the Corleones had bought one hotel and were planning to buy many more. Barzini was taking advantage of the peace between the five families, and was beginning to take over a lot of the Corleone family business in New York. Tessio and Clemenza wanted to fight Barzini before he became too strong, but Michael, who had spent long hours talking to Tom Hagen and his father, learning the family business, told them to be patient. At first, Tessio and Clemenza didn't like taking orders from Michael. They tried to talk to Don Corleone instead. But the old man said: 'Do you trust me?'

'Yes, Godfather,' Tessio and Clemenza replied.

'Then be a friend to Michael. He's head of the family now. Do as he says.'

One afternoon, Michael sat in the garden with his father. Don Corleone had put on a lot of weight and moved very slowly. He spent most of his time in the garden, looking after his plants, or just sitting under a tree, drinking wine, thinking about the past. But his mind was still sharp. Michael always came to him for advice.

'Be careful of Barzini,' he told Michael. 'He'll move against you first. He'll arrange a meeting with someone that you trust. He'll promise you safety. But at that meeting, he'll kill you.'

Don Corleone drank some red wine, and suddenly changed the subject. 'Are you happy with your wife and children?' he asked.

*'Be careful of Barzini,' Michael's father told him.*
*'He'll move against you first.'*

'Very happy,' Michael said softly. He wanted to hear more about Barzini, but he respected and loved his father too much to hurry him.

'That's good,' said Don Corleone. He looked around the garden for a moment with a sad look in his eyes, then said: 'I'm sorry I can't stop thinking about Barzini. It worries me. I always thought Sonny would be head of the family. I never wanted this for you. There just wasn't enough time . . .'

Michael gently touched his father's arm. 'Don't worry, Father,' he said. 'I'll take care of it.'

Don Corleone nodded, smiled to himself, then looked suddenly serious as if he had forgotten to tell Michael something important.

'What's the matter, Father?' Michael asked.

'Listen,' Don Corleone raised one finger. 'Whoever comes to you with this Barzini meeting – he's the traitor. Don't forget that.'

Then, standing with great difficulty, he touched Michael lovingly on the cheek and walked slowly back to the house, out of the sun.

♦

One Sunday morning, while the women were at church, Don Corleone was playing with his grandson among his tomato plants in the garden. As he tried to run away from the little boy who was chasing him, he suddenly found it hard to breathe. It was as if the sun had come down very close to his head. He stopped running and started to cough as he tried to get air into his chest. The little boy laughed, thinking this was part of the game. Don Corleone bent forward, coughing more and more, and then he felt it: an explosion of fire inside his chest. With a cry of pain, he fell back among his tomato plants, dead.

All his life, people had tried to kill him. They had failed. In the end, Don Vito Corleone died a natural death, playing with his grandson in his garden on a peaceful Sunday morning.

*In the end, Don Vito Corleone died a natural death, playing with his grandson in his garden on a peaceful Sunday morning.*

# Chapter 13   Traitor

At the funeral, Michael sat with his family as people walked past, one by one, throwing flowers on to his father's grave. Michael studied their faces carefully: Clemenza, Tessio, Enzo the butcher, Johnny Fontane, all the people that his father had helped in his long and dangerous life. Some of his enemies were at the funeral too. Barzini threw a red rose on to the grave, and lowered his eyes respectfully in Michael's direction. Michael stared at him coldly as he turned and walked away.

A few minutes later, Tessio walked up to Michael and whispered something in his ear. Michael stood up and walked away from the grave to hear what Tessio wanted to say.

'Barzini wants to arrange a meeting,' Tessio said. 'He says we can solve all our problems.'

'Did you talk to him?'

'Yes. I can arrange everything. Trust me.'

Michael looked at Tessio. He had known him all his life. He had always been like an uncle to him. But Michael remembered his father's words – 'Whoever comes to you with this Barzini meeting, he's the traitor' – and he felt a great sadness in his heart.

'All right,' Michael said quietly, and he returned to his seat by his father's grave. He told Tom, who was sitting next to him, about his conversation with Tessio.

Tom shook his head sadly. 'I always thought it would be Clemenza,' he said.

'No,' said Michael. 'This is a clever move, and Tessio's cleverer than Clemenza. But I'm going to wait. I've decided to be godfather to Connie's baby, and then I'm going to meet Barzini, Tattaglia and all the heads of the five families.'

He watched Tessio who was standing some distance away, shaking hands and talking with Barzini. He hadn't told Tom the whole truth. Tom was not a *Consigliere* any more, so he didn't know everything in the way that he used to. The truth was that Michael had already decided to kill all his enemies. They were going to die on the day he stood as godfather to Connie's child.

## Chapter 14   Michael Rizzi, Go in Peace

As Michael walked into the church with Kay, Connie, Carlo and the rest of the family, his men were all over New York, getting ready to kill his enemies. Pete Clemenza kissed his wife goodbye and left the house carrying a large flower-box under his arm. Michael's personal bodyguard, Albert Neri, was putting on a policeman's uniform. Clemenza's close friend, Rocco Lampone, was sitting with his eyes closed in a large hotel, while a man gave him a shave. Two other men who worked for the family were checking their machine-guns in a small, apartment room somewhere in a cheap part of the city.

♦

Kay stood in the church, Connie's baby sleeping in her arms. The priest spoke Latin and touched the baby's cheeks and mouth with water. Then he asked Michael: 'Do you believe in God the Father, the Maker of Heaven and Earth? Do you believe in Jesus Christ?'

Michael said: 'I do.'

♦

Albert Neri was standing on the pavement in his policeman's uniform. He was talking to the driver of a car which was parked in front of the Plaza Building, trying to make him move away. The driver shook his head and refused to move.

Pete Clemenza was running up a lot of stairs in a dark hotel, the flower-box under his arm. His fat face was hot and red, and he was very short of breath.

Rocco Lampone checked his face in the mirror, paid the man in the hotel who had given him the shave, and calmly walked out of the door.

The two men with machine-guns looked at each other and, without a word, walked out of their apartment.

◆

The baby in Kay's arms woke up and began to cry. He didn't like the water on his face.

◆

Barzini appeared at the top of the steps of the Plaza Building with his bodyguard. Looking down, he saw his driver arguing with a policeman on the pavement, so he sent his bodyguard down to find out what the problem was.

Rocco Lampone waited near the desk in the hotel entrance, and smoked a cigarette.

Pete Clemenza reached the top of the stairs and rested against a wall outside a lift, completely out of breath.

◆

'Michael Francis Rizzi,' the priest spoke to the crying baby. 'Do you refuse Satan, and everything that Satan does?'

◆

Clemenza waited outside the lift. Suddenly, the doors opened and a small, thin man with silver hair, a red flower in the buttonhole of his expensive suit, stepped out. It was Cuneo, one of the New York Godfathers who had been at the meeting with Don Corleone three years before. He stopped when he saw

Clemenza, a look of confusion on his face. Clemenza lifted his short, fat leg and kicked Cuneo hard in the stomach. Cuneo fell backwards into the lift. Clemenza quickly opened his flower-box and took out a large shotgun. He pointed it at Cuneo and fired.

♦

'I do refuse Satan,' Michael spoke quietly to the priest, answering for the baby. 'And everything that Satan does.'

The baby went on crying.

♦

A man in a white suit walked past the desk where Rocco Lampone was waiting. He was on his way out of the hotel. This was Stracci, another New York Godfather. As he was half-way through the revolving doors, Lampone ran from the desk and locked the door to stop it turning. Stracci was caught inside. He tried to push, but the doors wouldn't move. He hit the glass with his hands. He turned round and found himself face to face with the end of Rocco Lampone's gun. He put his hands up and pressed himself against the door behind him. Rocco fired and the bullets crashed through the glass of the door straight into Stracci's heart.

♦

Philip Tattaglia had left his bodyguards outside in the street while he had a secret meeting with his girlfriend in a small room in a cheap part of New York. This was his last mistake. As he was kissing her, the door burst open and two men with machine-guns rushed in. As Tattaglia looked around for his gun, the girl jumped to her feet and screamed. The gunmen opened fire and Tattaglia and the girl fell back in a shower of bullets. Then the gunmen left as suddenly as they had appeared, leaving behind them a smoke-filled room and two dead bodies in a pile of torn and bloody bedclothes.

♦

The priest held a silver spoon above the baby's head, and let drops of water fall on to the baby's face. '*In Nomine Patris, et Filii, et Spiritus Sancti*,' the priest said . . .

♦

. . . Barzini's bodyguard ran down the steps of the Plaza Building and called to the policeman, who was writing something in his notebook. The policeman put away his notebook, took out his handgun and shot the bodyguard dead. The driver of the car put up his hands but there was no pity in Albert Neri's heart. He killed him too. Barzini, who was half-way down the steps, turned and began to walk quickly back up towards the building. He was a proud man. He never liked to run too fast for anything, not even when his life was in danger. This gave Neri the time that he needed to go down on one knee, point his gun carefully up at Barzini, and shoot him three times in the back. Barzini stopped, as if in surprise, then fell backwards down the steps.

♦

Suddenly, inside the church, the baby stopped crying.

'Michael Rizzi, go in peace,' the priest said. 'And God go with you always. Amen.'

'Amen,' Michael Corleone said softly, and lowered his eyes, knowing that, by now, all his enemies were dead.


## Chapter 15   Family Business

As the family stood on the steps outside the church, Carlo Rizzi shook Michael's hand. 'Thank you, Godfather, thank you,' he kept saying, tears of happiness in his eyes.

'I was pleased to do it,' Michael said, then added, without smiling, 'Now, Carlo, could you go and wait for me in the house?

I'm afraid we can't go with our families to visit Las Vegas today. We'll have to wait here for a couple of days. You can join Connie and your children then, OK?'

'OK,' Carlo said. He knew better than to show he was unhappy. Michael had been very good to him. He had welcomed him into the family, he had been godfather to his son. He did whatever Michael wanted him to do. He never argued.

When Carlo had gone, Michael kissed his wife and his sister, and left them on the steps outside the church. He had more business to take care of.

♦

Tessio was ringing Barzini's office from the wall-phone in Tom Hagen's kitchen, not knowing that Barzini was already dead.

'Tell Barzini we're on our way to Brooklyn,' he said. After the call, he turned to Tom, who was waiting for him, and said: 'I hope Mike gets what he wants from the meeting tonight.'

'I'm sure he will,' Tom nodded seriously.

He followed Tessio out of the house. They were half-way across the street to Michael's house when they were stopped by a bodyguard.

'The boss says he'll come in another car,' the man said. 'He says you two can go before him.'

Tessio looked worried. 'He can't do that,' he said, turning to Tom. 'That spoils all my arrangements.'

Three more bodyguards appeared from nowhere and stood around him. Then Tom said gently: 'I can't go with you either, Tessio.'

Tessio understood everything immediately. He knew that he was going to die for trying to betray Michael. He looked at Tom sadly and said: 'Tell Mike it was only business. I always liked him.'

'He understands that,' Hagen nodded.

Tessio paused for a second. He was a brave man, but he

couldn't stop himself from showing Tom a moment of plain, human weakness. 'Tom, can you help me?' he asked. 'As a friend?'

Tom shook his head and looked away. He didn't want to show his feelings, but inside he felt sick. Tessio had always been the best soldier in the Corleone family. 'I'm sorry, Tessio, I can't do that,' he said, and walked away.

Tom watched from his window as the four bodyguards led Tessio towards a waiting car and drove him away for his meeting, not with Barzini, but with death.

◆

Carlo Rizzi was sitting in his front room, making a phone-call, when something made him turn round. Michael was watching him from the doorway. Tom Hagen and a bodyguard were standing quietly behind him. Carlo saw the icy look in Michael's eyes, and he felt his whole body go weak.

'Carlo, you have to answer for Sonny,' Michael said.

Carlo didn't answer. He stood up, pretending not to understand.

'You betrayed Sonny,' Michael continued in a cold, flat voice. 'Did you really think you could fool a Corleone? You played a game, didn't you? You made Sonny angry by hitting your own wife. You knew that he'd come to help her.'

Carlo began to shake with fear. 'I promise you, on my son's life, I'm innocent. Mike, don't do this to me, please!'

But Michael calmly made him sit down next to him. 'Barzini's dead,' he said quietly, not taking his eyes off Carlo's frightened face. 'Philip Tattaglia's dead too. Cuneo, Stracci, they're all gone. Today, I'm taking care of all family business. So don't tell me you're innocent. Don't lie to me.'

Carlo started to cry, but he didn't say anything. Tom Hagen gave him a drink, and Michael put a brotherly arm around his shoulder. 'Don't be afraid,' he said. 'I'm not going to kill you. You're my sister's husband. I'm your son's godfather. No. I'm going to throw you out of the family business. I'm putting you on a plane to Las Vegas to join your family. I want you to stay there. That's going to be your punishment. Now please, don't tell me you're innocent, because that insults my intelligence. It makes me very angry. Tell me what happened. Who killed Sonny? Barzini or Tattaglia?'

Carlo stopped crying and looked up with a sudden feeling of hope. He saw Michael's eyes close to his. They looked warm and full of forgiveness. He swallowed the rest of his drink and smiled at Michael with a grateful look in his eyes.

'It was Barzini,' he said quietly.

'Good. Good,' Michael said, nodding to himself. He stood up and turned towards the window. 'There's a car waiting for you outside,' he said. 'It'll take you to the airport. I'll call Connie to tell her you're coming.'

Carlo stood up and tried to speak. 'Michael, please . . .'

But Michael turned on him angrily, his eyes cold and hard again. 'Get out of here,' he said. 'I never want to see you again.'

When Carlo left the house, he saw two men putting suitcases into the back of his car. He got into the passenger seat and waited for someone to drive him away. He didn't see Pete Clemenza sitting quietly behind him in the back seat.

'Hello, Carlo,' Clemenza said.

Before Carlo could turn round, Clemenza threw a smooth thin cord around Carlo's neck and pulled hard. Carlo fought and tried to escape. His body jumped around like a fish on the end of a line. His foot crashed through the front window of the car, but Clemenza was too strong for him. He pulled the cord until it cut into Carlo's throat. A minute later, Carlo Rizzi was dead.

Michael, who had watched it all from the front of the house, turned away, followed by Tom Hagen. He had taken care of all the family business in one day. The Corleones were now the strongest family in New York. He had reason to feel proud.

♦

When Connie heard that her husband was dead, she flew back at once to see Michael. She ran straight into his office and screamed at him: 'You killed my husband! You waited until Papa died and then you killed him! You blamed him for Sonny. You always did. Everybody did. You never thought about me! What am I going to do?'

Michael sat quietly at his desk. Kay tried to calm Connie down, but Connie pushed her away, ran around the desk and started to kick and hit her brother, crying and screaming the whole time. 'You stood godfather to our baby! You cold-hearted killer! You animal! You...!'

Michael didn't try to move away. He let Connie scream at him and hit him. Finally, she was taken away into another room, and Michael was left alone with Kay in the office.

He walked around the room, feeling uncomfortable at the strange look Kay was giving him. She was shocked by what had happened. She was also a little afraid.

'She's gone crazy,' Michael tried to explain. 'Understandable, I guess...'

Kay could hear Connie screaming from the next room. She looked her husband in the eye and said: 'Michael, is it true?'

'Don't ask me about my business, Kay,' he replied.

'Is it true?' she repeated.

Michael repeated his reply.

When she asked him for the third time, he crashed his hand down on to the desk. 'Enough!' he shouted.

Kay lowered her eyes and bit her lip.

Finally, Michael said: 'All right. This one time. I'll let you ask me about my business.'

'Is it true?' she whispered.

Michael looked at Kay. He stood completely still. Then he

shook his head and softly answered: 'No.'

Kay was so happy that she almost started crying. She ran up to her husband and hugged him.

A few minutes later, she moved back and looked at him. 'I guess we both need a drink,' she tried to laugh.

She left the office to get a drink. She was about to take the two glasses back into the room when she saw several men entering the office from another door. One of them was Pete Clemenza, the funny little fat man she had first seen dancing at Connie's wedding many years before. She watched in silence as he lowered his head, kissed Michael's hand and said, in a deep, respectful voice: 'Don Corleone.'

Then someone gently closed the door, and Kay was left outside, alone. Her new life as the Godfather's wife had only just begun.

*Clemenza lowered his head, kissed Michael's hand and said, in a deep, respectful voice: 'Don Corleone.'*

# ACTIVITIES

## Chapter 1

*Before you read*

1 Look at the Word List at the back of the book. Find any new words in your dictionary. The find these words:

    **a** A gangster might put *this* round someone's neck to kill them.

    **b** The Godfather needs several of *these* to protect him.

    **c** You can listen or dance when *this* plays.

    **d** *This person* is not loyal to the boss.

    **e** When a member of the Mafia is killed, their family look for the killers to get *this*.

    **f** *This word* describes a gangster who always wants to start a fight.

    **g** When a person dies, his family and friends come to *this*.

2 Read the Introduction and answer these questions.

    **a** What has Michael Corleone done in his life when the story starts?

    **b** Why doesn't Don Corleone want Michael in the family business?

    **c** Where did writer Mario Puzo get his ideas for *The Godfather*?

    **d** Did Puzo think *The Godfather* was his best book?

    **e** Which two actors play Don Corleone in the Coppola films?

    **f** Which real people did Puzo use to make the character of Don Corleone?

    **g** Who do people think was the model for Johnny Fontane?

3 Write down five things you think you know about the Mafia. Compare your list with other students. Have you all written the same things?

*While you read*

4 Check this information about the Corleone family. Is it right (✓) or wrong (✗)?

    **a** Carlo Rizzi has just married the Godfather's daughter.   .....

    **b** Don Corleone has four sons – Sonny, Fredo, Michael and Tom.   .....

**c** Don Corleone has brought Tom Hagen up as a son.       .....

**d** Singer Johnny Fontane is Don Corleone's godson.       .....

**e** Kay already knows all about the Corleone family.       .....

**f** Michael doesn't work in the family business.       .....

**g** Don Corleone is sending Luca Brasi to California
with Johnny Fontane.       .....

*After you read*

5 Match the adjectives to the people they describe.

| | | |
|---|---|---|
| **a** | the wedding guests | • excited |
| **b** | Don Corleone | • famous |
| **c** | Johnny Fontane | • frightening |
| **d** | Kay Adams | • powerful |
| **e** | Fredo | • respectful |
| **f** | Luca Brasi | • weak |

6 If a Mafia member *makes an offer you can't refuse*, which of these
does he do?

**a** He offers to give you something very nice if you help him.

**b** He promises to hurt or kill you if you don't help him.

## Chapters 2–3

*Before you read*

7 How do you think Tom Hagen will behave with the boss of the film
company?

*While you read*

8 Choose the best words in *italics*.

**a** Jack Woltz *knows/doesn't know* who Tom Hagen works for at
their first meeting.

**b** Jack is much *more/less* welcoming to Tom at their second
meeting.

**c** Woltz *refuses/agrees* to do Don Corleone a favour.

**d** Johnny Fontane *stole/killed* Jack's girl.

**e** Jack finds *half-eaten fruit/a horse's head* in his bed.

**f** Virgil Sollozzo wants to get into the *guns/drugs* business.

**g** Sollozzo is already working with *Tom Hagen/the Tattaglia family*.

**h** *Nobody knows/Sonny and Tom know* about Luca Brasi's secret job for the Godfather.

**i** Bruno Tattaglia and Sollozzo murder Luca with *a knife/a cord*.

**j** Sollozzo *wants/doesn't want* to kill Tom.

**k** Fredo *gets help/cries* when his father is shot.

*After you read*

9 Work with another student. Have this conversation.

> Student A: You are Jack Woltz. You found the horse's head in your bed this morning. Say how you feel and ask a friend for advice.

> Student B: You are Jack's adviser. Ask questions about Tom Hagen and Don Corleone. Give Jack some advice.

## Chapters 4–5

*Before you read*

10 Discuss these questions.

**a** Who sent the men to shoot Don Corleone?

**b** Why did Virgil Sollozzo kill Luca Brasi?

**c** What is going to happen to Tom Hagen?

**d** Which person in Don Corleone's family will take over from him?

*While you read*

11 Put these words in the spaces.

angry   betrayed   driver   family business   kidnapped
know   message   New York   phone calls

**a** Michael's family don't know he and Kay are in ........................ .

**b** Sonny is ........................ with Pete Clemenza because he says that Vito is dead.

**c** Sonny is angry with his father's ........................ Paulie because he wasn't there.

**d** Sollozzo phones Sonny to tell him that he has ........................ Tom Hagen.

   **e** Sonny gets information about ........................ made by Paulie and Clemenza.

   **f** Sonny doesn't ........................ that Luca Brasi is dead.

   **g** Michael hasn't known about ........................ before now.

   **h** Don Corleone was ........................ by Paulie.

   **i** The dead fish ........................ is from Sollozzo.

*After you read*

**12** Michael shows important qualities in Chapter 5. Find an example for each of these qualities.

   **a** He doesn't tell people things they don't need to know.

   **b** He acts calmly.

   **c** He is very practical.

   **d** He says nice things to people.

   **e** He is brave.

   **f** He isn't a hothead.

## Chapters 6–7

*Before you read*

**13** Discuss and then write answers to these questions. Check the answers when you finish reading the book.

   **a** Is Michael and Kay's relationship over?

   **b** How will the Corleone family get revenge on Sollozzo and the Tattaglia family?

   **c** Will Sollozzo's men kill Don Corleone?

*While you read*

**14** Read the questions and write the names. Who:

   **a** did the Corleone family kill at 4 a.m.?  ........................

   **b** does Sollozzo want to meet?  ........................

   **c** is protecting Sollozzo?  ........................

   **d** is going to teach Michael how to kill?  ........................

   **e** is killed first?  ........................

   **f** dies second?  ........................

**15** Draw lines to make sentences.

a The police fight the
  New York families      in Sicily.

b Michael goes into hiding      before they marry.

c He stays with Don Tommasino      a café owner's daughter.

d He falls in love with      after McCluskey is killed.

e Michael and Apollonia
  cannot be alone      near the town of Corleone.

*After you read*

**16** Work with a small group of students. You are all guests at Michael and Apollonia's wedding. Talk about the wedding, the clothes, the food, the dancing, and Michael and Apollonia.

## Chapters 8–11

*Before you read*

**17** Discuss these questions.

a Will Michael and Apollonia have a happy marriage?

b Will Michael stay in Sicily?

c What has happened back in New York, do you think?

d Do you feel this is a calm moment before stormy times ahead?

e Two characters die in the next two chapters – who will they be?

*While you read*

**18** Are these sentences right (✓) or wrong (✗)?

a Carlo hurts Sonny's sister, but Sonny doesn't hurt
  Carlo.      .....

b Carlo beats Connie again, and Sonny plans to kill him.      .....

c Some gangsters are waiting for Sonny at the tollbooth.      .....

d Don Corleone wants to meet the heads of the other
  families.      .....

e Michael stays in Don Tommasino's house after Sonny
  is killed.      .....

f Don Tommasino betrays Michael.      .....

g The war was about the drugs business.      .....

**h**  Don Corleone does not agree to allow drug selling.        .....

**i**  Don Corleone promises to share his Government
      friends and not take revenge.                              .....

**j**  The other dons agree not to hurt Michael.                 .....

*After you read*

**19**  Work with another student. Have this conversation.

   *Student A*:  You are Kay. Michael has come back and asked you
                to marry him. He seems different. You don't like his
                family. Ask for advice from your friend.

   *Student B*:  You are Kay's friend. Ask her questions about Michael
                and his family. Give her your advice.

## Chapters 12–14

*Before you read*

**20**  Don Corleone is old. Sonny is dead. Fredo is weak. Will Michael
       make a good godfather? What qualities does he have that will
       help him?

**21**  Chapter 13 is called 'Traitor'. Who will be the traitor, do you think?
       Choose a name.

   **a**  Tessio              **d**  Carlo Rizzi
   **b**  Pete Clemenza       **e**  Enzo the butcher
   **c**  Tom Hagen           **f**  Johnny Fontane

*While you read*

**22**  Underline the mistakes in these sentences. Write the correct words
       in the spaces.

   **a**  Tessio and Clemenza respect Michael as
         much as Don Corleone.                         .........................

   **b**  Don Corleone is enjoying an easy life and
         his mind is weak.                             .........................

   **c**  Don Corleone is happy that Michael must
         be the head of the family.                    .........................

   **d**  Don Corleone warns Michael that there is
         a traitor in Barzini's family.                .........................

   **e**  Don Corleone dies a violent death.           .........................

**f** Pete Clemenza arranges the Barzini
meeting. ........................

**g** Michael tells Tom that he is planning to kill
all his enemies. ........................

**23** Draw lines to match the names, the crimes and the places.

| Name | Crime | Place |
|---|---|---|
| **a** Michael Corleone | shoots Stracci | in some revolving doors. |
| **b** Pete Clemenza | shoot Tattaglia | in New York. |
| **c** Albert Neri | arranges four deaths | in a cheap hotel room. |
| **d** Rocco Lampone | shoots Cuneo | on the Plaza Building steps. |
| **e** Michael's gunmen | shoots Barzini | in a lift. |

*After you read*

**24** Don Corleone dies a peaceful, natural death. He wasn't punished
for all his crimes over his life. Is this fair, do you think?

## Chapter 15

*Before you read*

**25** Michael has killed the heads of the four other New York families.
He has more family business to finish. Who is he going to kill next,
do you think?

*While you read*

**26** Choose the best answers.

  **a** Tessio isn't happy because …
    **1)** Barzini is dead.
    **2)** Michael changes arrangements.

  **b** Michael's bodyguards are going to kill Tessio because …
    **1)** he doesn't like Michael.
    **2)** he was going to betray Michael.

  **c** Michael kills Carlo Rizzi because …
    **1)** he beat Connie.
    **2)** he betrayed Sonny.

**d** Michael …
  **1)** tells Kay the truth about Carlo and Connie.
  **2)** lies to Kay about Carlo and Connie.

*After you read*

**27** Talk to other students. You are making a new film of *The Godfather*.
Which famous actors will you choose for these parts?
  **a** Don Vito Corleone       **d** Virgil Sollozzo
  **b** Michael Corleone        **e** Tom Hagen
  **c** Kay Adams               **f** Apollonia

**Writing**

**28** Imagine Michael doesn't lie to Kay at the end of the story. He tells
her that he ordered Carlo's death. What will Kay do? Write a new
ending.

**29** The gangsters in this story are all criminals. Are they all bad or do
they have some good qualities? Choose two or three characters
and list the good and bad things about them.

**30** Imagine Sollozzo's men do not shoot Don Corleone and he lives
for many more years. What kind of life does Michael have? How is
it different from his actual life? Describe it.

**31** The Mafia has its own rules about how to live. For example, *The
women in the family must never ask questions*. What other Mafia
rules do you learn from this story? Write the rules.

**32** If you are born into a Mafia family, it is difficult to live a life without
crime. Michael wants to stay out of the family business, but he
is drawn in. Think of other lives that are difficult to escape from.
Write your ideas.

**33** The police interview the fruit-seller in Chapter 3. He saw the
shooting of Don Corleone. Write the interview.

**34** You are a journalist. You walk past the Italian restaurant just after
Michael leaves (see Chapter 6). You go in and see the dead bodies.
Write a story for your newspaper. Remember this is the first time a
Mafia family has killed a New York police captain.

**35** You work for the police department. You are on duty on the day that Michael becomes godfather to Connie's son. Four killings take place in the city that day. Write the day report to give to your police captain.

**36** Find out about the St Valentine's Day killings in Chicago on 14 February 1920. This was a big fight between famous gangsters Al Capone and Bugs Moran. Write about what happened.

**37** You are Michael in Sicily. Write a letter to Kay. Say you are sorry that you left without saying goodbye. Try to explain why you had to leave quickly, without saying that you killed someone.

# WORD LIST

**Amen** a very old word often used in church, meaning 'It is true' or 'I agree'

**band** (n) a musical group

**betray** (v) to be disloyal to someone who thinks you are loyal

**betting** (n) trying to win money by guessing the results of future events such as horse races

**bodyguard** (n) someone whose job is to protect an important person

**bruise** (n/v) a purple or brown mark that you get on your skin if it has been hit

**butcher** (n) someone who works in a shop that sells meat

**cheek** (n) the soft round part of your face below each of your eyes

**cord** (n) a piece of thick string

**Don** (n) a title for the leader of a Mafia organisation

**favour** (n) something that you choose do for someone to help them

**funeral** (n) the event when a dead person's body is put under the ground or burnt

**godfather** (n) in the Christian religion, a man who promises to help a child, and to teach him/her Christian ideas; it is also a title for heads of Mafia organisations

**godson** (n) in the Christian religion, a male child that a godparent promises to help

**grape** (n) a small round green or purple fruit, often used for making wine

**hothead** (n) someone who does things too quickly without thinking

**hug** (v) to put your arms around someone to show love or friendliness

**huge** (adj) very big

**nod** (v) to move your head up and down to mean 'Yes'

**Papa** (n) Father

**pavement** (n) a walkway at the side of a road

**permit** (v) allow

**priest** (n) a person who is trained for religious church duties

**respect** (v/n) to have a good opinion of someone; to be **respectful** means to show *respect*

**revenge** (n) something that you do to hurt someone who has hurt you

**revolving** (adj) turning in a circle

**Satan** (n) the main enemy of God

**tollbooth** (n) a place where you pay to drive on a road

**traitor** (n) someone who does something that is very disloyal

**trust** (v) to believe that someone is honest and will not hurt you